BEAUTIFUL OTHERNESS

SHIRLEY SIMMONS

Printed in the United States of America
ISBN: 978-1-7368075-0-7 (Paperback)
ISBN: 978-1-7368075-1-4 (Hardcover)
ISBN: 978-1-7368075-2-1 (Digital)

Library of Congress Control Number: 2021937252

Published by Shirley B Simmons
ShirleySimmons@ShirleyBSimmons.com
Visit: www.ShirleyBSimmons for more information.

BEAUTIFUL OTHERNESS

CONTENTS

Acknowledgements 1
Sunbathing And Prosecco 3
Kim 11
Phillip 19
You're Too Good At This 23
Mary Whitmore 27
The Adoption 29
They Have To Pay 35
Disappeared 37
Logical Fallacy 47
The Visit 53
Best Day Ever 59
Damn You Phillip 63
Next 69
Happy By Default 77
Janice Cooper Aka "The Jet" 81
Run For Your Lives 87

New York Times And Long Hair 97
Euphoria 103
Seniors 109
School Daze 115
14k 121
Broken Hallelujah 127
Growing Pains 135
You Don't Have My Permission 147
A Big Ass Wad Of Money 155
Party, Party, Party 165
Hyped For Hollywood 175
Rollerblading In Buckhead 191
Grumpy Caterpillar 199
Stronger 207
Greyson Davenport 213
The Thin Old Man 227
Sometimes Life Has Other Ideas 233

Oth-er-ness

NOUN: The quality or state of being
other or different.

ACKNOWLEDGEMENTS

I AM DEEPLY GRATEFUL TO my husband Arland Michael Simmons for his endless enthusiasm on this book. Thanks for your creative contributions that were truly needed on this project. Your ongoing love, support and encouragement has inspired me for a lifetime.

To a former coworker Rose Marie Campbell who told me 25 years ago that I would be writing this book.

To my BFF Katrina King a long-time supporter and fan of everything I have ever done.

To my sexy housewife ladies who has been a solid rock for friendship, love and support.

To my sister in Christ Kiacha Christy for being the first one to read the original manuscript and providing honest feedback.

To my dear friend Homer Hartage with Hartage Publishing Company in Orlando, FL. He has been my mentor for many years, and I consider him my walking book of knowledge. Thank you so much for pushing me to finish this book and bringing it to completion through your editing services.

To Stephanie Outten, you are a jewel. Thank you so much for making this process feel seamless and making this book a success. I appreciate everything your team at Cocoon to Wings Publishing did to bring my book project to life.

SUNBATHING AND PROSECCO

WHO AM I? MOST people only have to look toward home to find the answer to that question. Others have to sift through pieces of broken and scattered history. Sometimes the pieces they find can be painful and cling like wet clothing.

For me, there were many loose ends and pieces that didn't fit until I began to put them all together. I discovered my uniqueness through my history. I found out who I am and this is my story.

"What a life, Kennedy!" I breathed deeply, basking shamelessly in the golden sun as it kissed my perfectly bronzed skin.

I've always loved the outdoors, so now, whenever a free moment is afforded to me, you can find me at the beach, boating or at my latest hobby--playing tennis.

Reaching out for another sip of my Prosecco, I thought, *"Now this is life at one of its finest moments."*

I was in the backyard of our Windermere, Florida home, the community of Who's Who, of the elite and the wealthy, with its share of sprawling mansions, docking piers and celebrity residents.

If you know anything about Florida summers, you know they can run from May to October, and some years until the end of November. But you were sure to have eight months of perfect boating weather.

And every weekend during those months, nearby Bird Island filled with boaters eager to party.

My peace was mildly disturbed as more boats sailed in; their early arrival charged with the hope of getting a prime location.

There was a time when I was free to do whatever I wanted. Back in those days, I was selfish and spoiled and often only thought of myself. But now my time was always accounted for. This was the first Saturday morning I could remember that I did not have to attend a meeting or some other boring function. Today was all mine.

I had every intention of taking full advantage of the day. Sunbathing and Prosecco were the weapons of choice. I knew the day would pass quickly, and by early evening I would be preparing myself for tonight's gala. I was smiling. All the hard work and dedication I had put forth the last three years was bearing fruit.

Slipping back into the serenity of the lake house I began to wonder what my life could have been. As if on cue, I had an unconscious trigger--a 6x6 cell, cold metal bars, that pungent deathly smell of hopelessness, that dark, suffocating….

"Get yourself together, Kennedy!" I mentally pulled myself back to the present. This was going to be my night. I'm over all that. I'd had my closure and no trigger from the past was going to spoil this day for me.

Closing my eyes, I leaned back deep into the cushion of the pool lounge chair and exhaled a deep shaky breath.

I grew up in a small town where everybody knew everybody else's business. With who I am--who I was—my failing would have been the topic of conversation for years. But I didn't fail.

"Those fools would have loved to see me in prison just like Phillip," I murmured aloud. Ironically, instead of having prison guards instructing my every move behind bars, I give security guards Christmas presents and they guard the gates of my secured Isleworth home.

"In Jesus name."

Still, the past cuts deep. The simple thought of Phillip's demons had tormented me on and off over many years. And right now, with all the excitement of the awards dinner, it was nearly bringing me to tears. But the Prosecco was doing its job. My mind drifted to some of my innermost thoughts, all the advice that I had received to get me to this very moment. Advice about life and how to succeed at it. Advice such as learn how to have fun in life because most people with high IQ's generally find the world boring and tedious. Good stuff. And just one of the little bits of wisdom I've learned to live by.

The most interesting part of that advice is that my mother—the person who shared that with me--never had me tested, so I have no idea what my IQ really is. Maybe she just knew I would get bored with most things in life. She also told me to be open to experiences, knowing I could very well be the stupidest person in the room. And my favorite, which I can still hear my mother's voice saying, is "Life is like shooting porn; it's not how it starts or ends but it's all the action in between that makes it worthwhile."

Thinking about it, my mother's wisdom had prepared me for almost every obstacle I had faced. For a woman with no education, she sure was astute. She was clever and spot on with her advice even if I did not take notice of it immediately. That porn reference was not hers. She was a straightforward good Christian through and through, who has never seen porn in her life, so the reference to her quote is ironically comical but true.

Uninhibited freedom was something that I had been fortunate to have most of my life even if I was blindly unaware of it. I had been free to do what I wanted even with parental parameters and restrictions. Back then I did not know any other way, and today I wouldn't have it any other way.

I took another sip of the bubbly and casually took off my bikini top. Somehow my perky breasts have managed to defy gravity. I eased myself back down to get the full magic effects of the sun and was soon back to tranquility, serenaded by the morning breeze. All the distracting thoughts had dissipated.

"Nothing will disturb this beautiful morning!"

My mind began running through thoughts of my acceptance speech for the Central Florida Woman of the Year Award. Receiving this prestigious award made me nervous. Was I deserving? Could fleeing from my past and leaving the place I was born be misconstrued as shame instead of perseverance? Does my compassion for the adopted, homeless, and underprivileged please my critics? This award was just another trophy I would be collecting to symbolize another achievement of this empire we had built, yet this one was special to me.

I never went into doing this work with the notion of receiving awards and accolades. When I started, I never dreamed of recognition. I just wanted to make a change in the way I was living and give scholarships to a couple of deserving kids.

Life was absolutely perfect. The hour quickly passed, with only the waves of the lake and the pool's waterfall occasionally diverting me.

A Drab Café & Lounge music mix took my mind far away--away from all the frantic, overstretched parts of my life. My mind and body were in a place of bliss. As I floated in my thoughts, I pictured myself amongst the sand dunes and salty air of a secluded beach, sandpipers running back and forth avoiding the waves, my hair a beach mess.

"Mom!" I opened my eyes to see my beautiful daughter standing over me. "Mom, what shoes should I wear?" Kylie proclaimed holding a pair of sandals and a pair of Monica Chang heels.

"Well, there's my precious daughter!" I glanced at her over my shoulder. "Take both pairs but wear your heels."

"But I'm so tall with the heels. I feel like everyone is staring at me when I wear them."

"Kylie, sweetheart, plenty of women would love to have your height. You act as if you're six feet tall when you're only five feet seven. Trust me, that's a wonderful height for a beautiful young lady."

"Are you sure, Mom? Besides, it is so frustrating being the tallest girl in the room."

"Very sure, Kylie! When there is no need for you to have on the heels, change into your sandals."

With a pause and a smile, Kylie swung her hair imitating me. "Well, I'm off to my Charmette Ivy meeting, and the next time you see me I'll be addressed as President Kylie Davenport." Kylie raised both perfectly manicured eyebrows as her lips formed into a smile. "By the way, where is Dad?"

"Finishing up his swim." I pointed toward the lake.

Kylie curled her lips and frowned in disapproval. "I would never swim in that lake again. There are alligators in there, and things are always touching you." She rubbed the goosebumps from her arms. "I love you, Mom! By the way, you do know they can see you from the island." Kylie kissed me and began to dart off as she tossed a towel over me.

"Wait! Make sure you are home before four o'clock," I called after her. "The stylist and his team will be arriving to do our hair and makeup. I want us to be perfect this evening!"

Kylie was an only child like I was. Being raised as an only child, I always wanted several children of my own. I always thought I would have at least three. But life had other ideas. Greyson, my husband, and I tried several times, each time ending in miscarriages. It was my desire for Kylie to have siblings so that she would not have to feel like she was alone, like I sometimes used to.

Greyson and I tried to raise her with boundaries and faith. There was no way I could allow her to have the freedom that I was allowed at her age, and I would never tell her about Phillip. No child needs that baggage.

I removed the towel before falling back into the comfort of the lounge. "That child thinks she is the parent." I shook my head and laughed.

Reaching for the glass, I took another sip of Prosecco and began to adjust my swimsuit bottoms. Having double tan lines is so unlike a lady. Releasing every thought in my mind, I gave in to the calm summer morning.

"How is your morning, beautiful?" Greyson stood there tall and handsome in his orange and blue swim trunks, dripping wet and shaking the water from his hair, muscles glistening in the sun.

I opened my eyes and quickly took another swallow, then leaped to my feet, and with arms extended and my fingers dancing, I fell into his arms. "Honey, how was your swim?"

"It was a good swim. You're so dramatic," Greyson smiled.

I had been this way with Greyson ever since our first date. It was one of the things that he admired about me. I was dramatic and he was romantic, yet somehow it worked, and quite well.

"I got an early start and didn't want to wake you," said Greyson.

Kissing his chest, I looked up at him batting my eyes to get all his attention. "Kylie has already left for Charmette Ivy." I pulled Greyson toward me, my naked breasts smashing against his chest.

"You're so beautiful." He held me close. "You know that they can see you from the island, right Kennedy?"

"So I've been told. I'm certain I'm not the only woman to sunbathe topless on this lake," I replied.

Greyson smiled slyly. "Kennedy, I'm certain that you're the only one missing a top.

"What about Sarah, Bethany or Mary? No one thinks twice about them sunbathing topless so why should it matter if I do it? Besides, there are not a lot of boats on the lake this morning," I waved my hand toward the lake, "and we paid a lot of money to live here. I think I have the right to do as I please.

"But enough about this lake and the people who live on it. Earlier I was thinking about my life, all the challenges and victories in it. And how it all led up to being here with you and getting this award tonight."

Greyson lowered his head and kissed me on the neck, "Have I heard these stories before? Wait, do not answer that. I learn something new about you every time we talk about your life, so I would love to hear all about it, but first I'm off to take a shower."

I grabbed the bottle of Prosecco, took his hand and followed him. "Well I think that it's great that we still communicate after all these years of marriage. It warms my heart."

"So do I, babe. We both work really hard, and we work hard at our marriage. I am fine hearing repeat stories of your past. It is your past that made you the Kennedy I love. I never want to be one of those couples who stop talking and nurturing their marriage. We get to make the rules for how this marriage will work. Nothing frustrates me more than hearing married people giving bad advice about marriage and communication.

"Can't do this! You must do that, or whatever senseless, ill-advised, unwanted nonsense they are pushing. You always hear them saying the key to marriage is communication. But I think people shouldn't give limited advice; they should give examples to help others understand what they mean. Communication starts before the fighting; you communicate so that you don't fight, and if you are fighting, you better pray that one of you doesn't stop fighting, because if that happens… the marriage is over.

"I refuse to be one of those married guys who's always out without his wife or always with his sidepiece because he is tired of talking or being around his wife. Nope, not going to be me. But don't get me going on that subject. Besides, with you in my garden there are more peaceful skies. So, please tell your story."

"Ok, hun, please don't get started! Some of this you have heard but let me continue telling you all about it, ok?"

Just before stepping into the seclusion of our outdoor shower, I dropped my swimsuit bottoms.

KIM

Kim stared at the bag for what seemed like an eternity. The thought of leaving it all behind was the one thing that had been on her mind for the last six months. She had tried to brush the thoughts off as simply being emotional. Her husband, Edward, was not helping the situation much either. He was constantly telling her to pull it together and pointing out everything she did wrong. For all he knew and cared, he was providing for his wife and children, and as far as he was concerned, that should have been enough. He had worked hard to give her a house, car, and income to take care of the children, so why should she be unhappy? She had everything. However, on this day the postpartum was real and it was about to win.

The morning had begun like the countless other mornings--wake up at six, make love to Edward, prepare breakfast and lunch for him, see him off to work, then get the children fed and off to school. Only it was summer and there was no school.

"There never seems to be time for Kim," she muttered under her breath. "Even when I go to the bathroom there's a child attached to me."

Today was different. Kim had made what would turn out to be a life-altering decision. She stood there shoving clothing into luggage for herself, her oldest son and her two-year-old daughter. She then drove to her in-laws and asked if her other three children could stay with them while she went to the market. And with that in place, her journey began.

Kim longed to be carefree and unburdened. She couldn't bear the thought of living the slow Mississippi country life forever. She loved Edward but felt it was her right to have the life she wanted. Prior to her marriage she could always blend in and out of her two worlds. The two worlds made Kim's life complete. Her mother was black, and her father was white, so in one world she was white and the other she was black. This did not go over so well in the South, so she was sent off to be raised by relatives.

Even though she most closely resembled a white woman, she saw herself as black. Her fair skin, sandy brown hair and hazel eyes were an ally. By the time Kim was a teenager she had learned the benefits of her complexion as well as its downfalls. It allowed her in doors blacks could not walk through; it allowed her to attend schools that blacks couldn't. In the minds of her white classmates, she was one of them, so she was able to see and hear all the darkest secrets people harbored. But that all changed with her marriage, a marriage to a black man, Edward; and as far as most white people in the South were concerned, she was officially black from that point forward, and it didn't matter how fair her skin was.

But Kim had been feeling increasingly depressed, something that seemingly did not exist in 1970s. No one really gave depression any thought, especially if you were black. There was no doctor to turn to for help; at best you were simply called crazy.

Kim continued driving to Florida; she felt this was her only way out. She wanted more than the life of a wife and mother. She missed the comforts of her camouflage; she missed the freedom that came with being white. She wanted a break from it all. But she had nowhere else to go but to her mother's house. She didn't want to have to listen to what her mother had to say about her leaving Edward, but as she pulled up to her mother's house, Kim knew she would have to deal with it. She was willing to sacrifice to have her time away from Edward and the other kids.

Kim's mother was not that surprised to see her when she opened the door. She was aware of Kim's struggles with her identity and she knew that Kim was only truly happy when she was able to be black on her terms and white when it was convenient. For years she observed how Kim was able to navigate her identity between the two races. She feared how the decision of choosing one would ultimately affect her daughter. Had the day finally come?

"I have been waiting for this day for a long time, Kim. What do you need me to do?" They hugged as Kim, baby in tow, walked in the door with two suitcases and her son tugging at her leg.

"Just a place to stay, Mom."

"Well, what did Edward say about you leaving? Wait! Don't tell me you didn't let him know?" With both hands on her head. "Oh, my lord! That man must be a wreck. You didn't tell him you were leaving, and you have his kids?"

"I'm sure he's on his way here as we speak. I just need some time to sort things out. I feel like I'm going crazy. I have no life now, Mom. All I do is take care of Edward and these kids, and I have stopped bonding with the baby. Something is definitely wrong with me, Mom."

"Well, you have to work this out with Edward, but you are more than welcome to stay as long as you need."

That was all Kim needed to hear. If her mother did not mind her staying, she was going to use the time to reflect on life and what she wanted out of it. Edward was not going to be happy, but he was not her concern at that point. All she wanted was some of her mom's home cooking and for her mom to take the kids so that she could rest after the long drive.

Edward had come home after a long day of work. He saw a note by the phone and picked it up as he walked through the house looking for signs of Kim or the kids. When he didn't see anyone, he walked back toward the kitchen to read the note.

"Baby, it's Momma! Call me, please. Kim came by earlier and dropped off the kids asking if your daddy and I could watch them for a bit. She did not say when she was coming back, but she did take John and Rebecca with her. Let me know if you need me to feed them or if you're going to pick them up before dinner."

Edward walked back toward the phone. That's when he noticed an envelope with his name written in Kim's handwriting. To him, the room was eerily silent, and his hands shook as he picked it up.

"Edward, I'm leaving for a while to get my head together. I do not like who I have become. I do not think you like it either. It is all too much--life, marriage, kids. I feel like I have no purpose. I am going to my mother's house for a while. I have John and Rebecca with me and left the others with your parents. I know you and they will take good care of them. Please just give me this time. I will let you know when and if I am coming back. —Kim

Kim's actions did not sit well with her husband; the initial shock rapidly turned to anger the more Kim's leaving crossed his mind. Edward must have read the goodbye letter twenty times, each time desperately searching for some hidden explanation for her departure.

"I can't believe her!" he grumbled loudly as he read the letter again. As angry as he was, he remembered his mother's note. He grabbed his keys and jumped back in the car to pick up his kids. He returned home and got the kids settled for bed since his mom had already given the children dinner. He sat down and tried to eat from the plate his mom had fixed for him.

A couple of days had passed with not even a call from Kim to ask about the kids. Edward had been trying to be respectful by not calling her, but enough was enough. And with three kids constantly asking, "Where is Mom?" his anger rattled him so much that he was compelled to go and retrieve her.

"How could she leave? Why would she leave?" Edward shouted to no one as he approached the Alabama-Florida state line. The drive to Florida was a long boring commute, and the anger did not make the drive any easier. He was even more pissed because he had to take a couple of days off work and leave the kids with his parents again. When he arrived at Kim's mother's home, Edward knew the conversation would be tense and contentious, but he had prepared himself the entire 600-mile drive to Florida.

When Kim heard a car door slam outside the window, her gut told her it was Edward. She steadied her breath and held onto the doorknob for a minute before opening the door. He stormed in walking right past her and paced the floor not saying anything. His anger and frustration were evident in his breathing and stride. Kim was not surprised by this. In fact, she'd been expecting it. Any husband would react the same way.

Was she wrong in her approach to how she left? Without a word except for a note on the phone table? Like the footnote in a book, somewhat relevant, but not really necessary to the story. A sidebar in life's unraveling mystery. Maybe she should have waited until he got home from work to tell him in person, but she knew he wouldn't understand. She knew that would have only led to a huge argument, and she would not have been able to deal with that. And she knew she didn't even understand why she was feeling the way she did, so how could she possibly have articulated it to Edward?

Kim began to cry before she took a seat at the table. Edward's arrival brought her back to the emotional place she was trying to escape. She could see the anger he carried on his face; she even noticed his trembling hands as he cautiously approached. The idea of running out of the house crossed her mind several times, but she knew it was time to let Edward know her true feelings.

"Hello, Kim."

"Hi, Edward." Her voice was trembling with the inner fear of not knowing what was happening to her.

"May I have a seat so that we can talk?"

"Sure."

Before taking a seat, he retrieved a box of tissues from the living room placing them on the kitchen table between them.

"What are you doing, Kim? Why are you in Florida? Go get your things. We are going home!"

Edward did not yell but Kim could tell he was angry. Edward was not a violent man, but her mind raced trying to collect her thoughts. The idea of him yanking her up from the table, dragging her to the car, with her kicking, screaming and fighting, played in her head.

"I cannot do that, Edward."

"Kim, your family needs you. Now get your ass up."

"I cannot do that Edward, and please don't start cussing."

"I'm sorry, Kim, but what are you doing?"

"I need help, Edward. I mean, I need to fix myself."

Sensing that anger and force were not going to help the situation, he tried a different approach. He spoke calmly. "We will get you the help you need back in Mississippi."

"Edward, I can't go back to Mississippi, not right now."

"Why, baby?"

"I'm constantly sad or overwhelmed. I spend most of my days crying when you are at work, and when I am not crying, I'm yelling at the kids. The smallest things set me off and make me angry. It could be as simple as them asking, 'What's for dinner?' I know they can sense something is wrong with their mommy." She wrung her hands as she spoke. Her nerves were frazzled, and she was constantly on edge.

"I just feel inadequate. When I hold our baby, I start to feel like anyone but me could take care of her. I'm telling you! Something's not right, Edward," she wailed, "and I do *not* have to tell you how things are going with you and me. You're constantly telling me to pull it together!"

Edward began to see that his wife was in a dark place and it frightened him. He tried not to think of all the horrible possibilities that could take place if Kim continued the way she was.

"For the sake of everyone, you, me, and the children, you have to let me fix myself even if it hurts. Give me six months, please!"

Edward was, by this time, exhausted and defeated. They'd been at it for almost an hour and he finally surrendered without any further confrontation. It had been a long, challenging conversation and nothing he said convinced her to have a change of heart. Kim was beholden to her decision to abandon her family–temporarily at least. In her mind she was not forsaking them but doing what she needed to do to get herself back to feeling like a mother and wife, regardless of how it appeared to anyone else. At the end of the conversation, he persuaded her to let him return to Mississippi with the other two children so that she could focus on getting the help that she was in search of. She agreed. But secretly, Edward was concerned for those two children. Was Kim in such a bad place that she might harm them? Was her mother up to the task of looking after them and being around every minute just in case Kim did something unspeakable?

Her mother, who had been eavesdropping from the back room, began gathering the kids' clothes and getting them ready to leave with their father. Kim walked to the back, smirked at her mom for eavesdropping, and then quickly hugged her for getting the kids ready. Kim had the kids give their grandmother a hug before bringing them out to Edward.

He held onto his kids with his head held low. With a kiss on the cheek and a whispered, "Goodbye," Kim's quest to heal herself began.

PHILLIP

PHILLIP RUSHED ACROSS TOWN to collect his final payments for the day. What little traffic there was seemed to be on every route he was taking. Time was not on his side. The last thing he wanted was to have his father question his ability to do the job. Running and collecting numbers had become a pivotal part of the family business and Phillip had received the job by default. Even if it was a form of illegal lottery, there were a lot of people who depended on their winnings.

The person at the lowest level on the totem pole usually collected the numbers, and Philip was at the bottom. He was not his father's first or last choice for collecting numbers and money; his brothers—who would have been chosen over him--had taken different paths. One was enlisting in the military and the other had become a minister. So that left Phillip and his sister, and "the old man" surely wasn't going to have his daughter involved in that part of his affairs.

Phillip was the hot head of the four children. He was that child who kept you in prayer, and as much as you pulled for him you just knew he would find a way to screw it up. At some point his anger was going to get the best of his better judgment and he would find himself in trouble. So far, he had been fortunate; all of his run-ins with the law had not caught up with him yet. But the old man could see that something had changed in Phillip.

Phillip's drafting into the army in 1969 did not come as a surprise. If you were an able-bodied male of age it was simply a matter of time before you would receive a draft letter. His pops tried to prepare Phillip for what awaited him, but a black infantry squad being sent to the front line was a difficult conversation to have with a farm boy.

Phillip dug his trench a foot deeper than he was ordered; he figured a foot deeper could not hurt. Deeper was better, right? He would be lower when the bullets sailed over.

He was at the base of Hill 937, located at the Jungle Hill Mountain in South Vietnam. His platoon nervously awaited their orders to advance up the hill. They could feel the ground shifting from the heavy artillery being used on the enemy. The mountains' foliage had been stripped away--defoliated by chemical means. Agent Orange it was called. It was a strategy used to expose the enemy and their bunkers, and it gave Phillip a clear view of the destruction that he faced.

The men slept in the trenches, and the second day passed with him looking from his trench; he could hear the screams of the dying crying for help. Those who could be rescued were carried past his trench; their mangled bodies horrified him. Phillip's experiences as a tough guy had prepared him to kill everything in sight; his fear turned to rage. That rage had replaced all other emotions that Phillip had on that hill. He no longer thought of his parents, his brothers and sister or the small town. Kill or be killed was all he focused on.

Daybreak on the third day, it all ended. United States forces had taken control of the hill and Phillip never got the opportunity to kill. But the military and Vietnam had changed him. He was a far different person from the skinny, somewhat timid kid who left for the army. During his enlistment he had grown two inches. His shoulders had become broad and strong, and his jaw and chin chiseled. He was a warrior. And his new appearance was now just as intimidating as his often erratic, unstable personality.

When Phillip returned home from his stint in the military, "the old man" did his best to control Phillip by having him work the family-owned bar. He was still sent to collect the numbers and payment, and on those days, Phillip was free of his father's supervision. But it was not long before the complaints began. Phillip had begun stealing hundreds of dollars a week. His crime was not elaborate at all; he simply didn't pay if someone won. If someone complained, he threatened them or assaulted them. Because of his unpredictable behavior upon coming home from the army, which was now evident to anyone who knew him, there was often chatter in town that it was only a matter of time before the dark side of Phillip would arise, so many had stopped doing business with him and his father.

This put his father on damage control. Phillip's actions were costing him money and credibility; he could not afford to have those actions affecting his other businesses: the bar and the farm. Both had been worked by his family for three generations. He'd sat on the same barstool every day after school since he was old enough to climb up on it. It had been his old man's pride and joy. The farm was hard work, but it brought in money, and with two sons gone off now, it would be hard enough to keep it going without the extra hands. The bar was easy enough to run, but word of mouth got around quickly in this town. Joe, Phillip's pop, was well-loved in the neighborhood, but even that wouldn't save the bar if Phillip continued to drive away customers by cheating them. If he didn't stop it now, it wouldn't be long before it would go under. Outside of his children, the farm and the bar were what gave him the most pleasure in life. It was to those places that he devoted most of his love and attention.

Phillip's father enjoyed knowing that the black community looked up to him and the white folks respected him. The number-running business was simply a way of making easy money. It did not take much of his time, and it compensated for the off seasons when the farm didn't produce. He'd always run an honest business, paying when he needed to. He'd never cheated anyone. But now things had changed and Phillip was the cause.

"Come in, Phillip, and have a seat."

"What's up, Pop?"

He had taken a seat in the same chair he'd sat in too many times before to count. This had become an all too familiar occurrence for Phillip. Screw up, face the consequences from his father.

"I'm getting complaints, Phillip."

"Yeah, people are always complaining when they don't win."

"Don't interrupt me again, boy. People are complaining that you are not paying them their winnings, and on top of that you are threatening them. Now I am very much aware of you, let us just say, coming up short. And I cannot have that! It is not good business. How much have you taken? And don't you lie because I know the answer."

"If you know the answer, why are you asking?"

"Phillip, you don't get to ask the questions, and right now I'm not amused."

'Twelve hundred, Pop."

"You do know if this were anywhere else this conversation would go way different, or God forbid you had done this to the wrong man. Phillip, certain people will kill you for what you've done."

"What is it you want me to do?"

"Phillip, the people in town, I mean the poor in this town, depend on every dime that they have. So, it means everything to me if someone takes their last bit of money and gambles it with me. It means they trust and respect me. The bar and farm run on honesty, and just because this number running is illegal, it does not mean I run it without integrity. It is my name, Phillip. It's our name that's at stake."

Pop reached into his overalls and pulled out a manila envelope. In it were Phillip's instructions. "Take this and pay everyone that's been hit. Once you're done, return to the bar. You're off number pickup, Phillip."

"Come on, Pop, don't you think you're overreacting?"

The old man stood from behind his desk. "Boy, you can close the door on your way out. And the twelve hundred you essentially stole from me will be taken out of your paycheck. Don't think for one minute that you've gotten away with that part of your scam."

YOU'RE TOO GOOD AT THIS

If you were to ask my biological mother, Kim, whether she considered the ramifications of any of her actions knowing she was involved with someone so violent, I am sure she would have said no. From what I know of her she was a smart, determined woman. If she wanted to do something, she would figure out a way to get it done. She had a level of fearlessness that you had to have to do some of the things she did during that time, including dating Phillip. But I imagine if you were to stop and ponder the ramifications of every action, you probably would never do anything.

I have been told on several occasions that she was informed to stay clear of Phillip; that going out with him was a dangerous, crazy, reckless thing to do. And falling in love with him could prove to be life altering, and not in a good way. A million things had to go right for their relationship to make it. Surely, she must have known this was a bad idea. She was supposed to be smart. But she could never walk away from her relationship with him. For the life of me I can't make any sense of it.

Phillip tried to hide his frustration over being removed from collecting numbers. It had been two months since his last pickup, but it felt like a year. He hated the confines of the bar; he hated his punishment. No matter how many people came in, no matter the excitement, the hours seemed to creep along. But it all changed the day he looked out the window of the back room and spotted the most beautiful woman he'd ever seen sitting at the bar.

Kim had never been in the bar before. In fact, it was the first time she had stepped away from her mother's home since she'd left Edward and the kids. For the last three months Kim had diligently worked on her recovery. Every day consisted of meditation and exercise along with a change in diet. Both Kim and her mother were proud of the improvements she was making. For the first time in months, she was happy; her new routine had her youthful enthusiasm returning.

However, Kim was aware she had a long way to go. Every day she told herself things would get better. She missed her children and Edward. The feeling of missing her family occurred more and more. Even though she felt that way, she was still in no position to please her husband or parent their children. So, she did not call Edward, nor did she return any of his calls.

This was the first day Kim felt well and confident enough to be away from her mother's home. There were no worries of her past, no worries about her race and no thoughts of her family.

Kim had only chosen this particular bar because of its proximity to her mother's home. She had noticed it once while they were out driving and made a note in her mind to stop in when she felt ready.

That day, she decided it was time to venture out. She told herself she would have a quick drink and be on her way.

As Kim sat fondling her tumbler filled with cranberry and vodka, Phillip stared, fascinated with the beautiful lady at the bar. He studied her posture and every move from the back room. Kim sat alone at the end of the bar, oblivious to the man in the back room, innocent and unaware of the effects of her beauty. Just fifteen minutes prior she had been home, agitated and bored. She had not taken the time to change clothes. She quickly pulled her hair up into a high ponytail, which made her cheekbones appear to look more angular and her neck longer. She swiftly put on her sandals. The yellow polka-dotted dress she was wearing was the same one she had quickly put on to answer the door earlier.

Even after all the children she had birthed; Kim didn't look like she'd even had one kid let alone five. She still had the sprinter's physique she had in high school when she ran track.

Watching Kim, Phillip seemed to be in a trance. He was a tall, handsome brown skinned guy who normally did not have a problem approaching women. In fact, most women found him extremely attractive. But Kim's beauty had him stuck and thrown off his game. Phillip did not know how he should approach her. It was clear that she was not from the town, so he said a quick prayer with the hope that she was not just visiting.

A simple introduction was what he settled on as he made his way over. Kim took the introduction casually, but his persistence and smile eventually got to her and she began to lighten up. She was not surprised when Phillip approached her. He was the bartender, after all. But all during his introduction all she could think of was not sounding nasally. She hoped her Mississippi accent would not make her sound too country, even though she was sitting in a bar in the Deep South. Before she knew it, Phillip had taken a seat next to her and she was giving away more information about herself than she wanted to relinquish.

"I need to go, and you're too good at this, Phillip."

"Have one more drink with me," his voice was laced with desperation.

"Phillip, I really need to be on my way," Kim whined and smiled at the same time.

"Well, let me walk you to your car and we can exchange numbers. I just have to know more about you." That should have been a red flag for her, but she was still not on track with her normally great instincts.

Phillip escorted Kim to her car, and with that simple exchange a forbidden relationship was formed, a relationship that would change both of their lives forever.

MARY WHITMORE

A DEEP SENSE OF PANIC fell over her. She tossed and whimpered in her sleep. Once again, the Lord had spoken to her while she slept. Yet this time, for some reason, his words frightened her.

"Get ready," were the only instructions given. Mary sat up trembling from His command. Unsure if she was sweating from menopause or fear, she reached for the glass of water on the nightstand. The sheets were slightly damp under her.

Her husband, Earl, gave a purring snore with every exhale, completely unaware she was leaving their bed. Ever since his retirement from the railroad a year earlier she made sure not to disrupt his sleep. After twenty-seven years of odd hours and late shifts, the last thing Mary wanted to do was disrupt him as he slept peacefully.

Still rattled, she made her way to the kitchen and started a pot of coffee before returning to the bathroom to begin her shower. Their entire marriage she had made every attempt to be completely obedient to the word of God. She and Earl had eagerly prayed for a child, right up to the point of when her body was no longer able to conceive. There were many times she contemplated giving up, but Jesus was all she knew. So, any thought of abandoning Him was quickly rebuked.

Mary's knuckles turned white as she firmly gripped the handle in the shower. She desperately tried to push through her fear. She knew the words spoken to her were real. However, she did not know what she was to get ready for and that frightened her deeply.

She cleared her throat and spoke, "Father, I'm ready."

Earl entered the kitchen and headed straight toward the coffee pot, pouring himself a cup. Mary sat baffled at the table because he normally waited for her to bring him coffee and the paper.

Taking a sip of his coffee, he stared around the kitchen. "This room, just like every other room in this house, is too quiet and too neat. Nothing is ever out of place. I think we need a dog."

Still focused on the dream, Mary paused and walked over to him. Stopping just a foot from Earl, she stared at him with her large brown eyes. "A dog, Earl? I mean can we wait and have this conversation later?"

"I know I don't have the right to make that decision alone, and I don't want to persuade you on the idea. I just think we need a change around here, Mary. A dog might bring a little welcomed chaos to our lives. It's not that I'm unhappy with anything really, just a little bit in a rut. I guess it's just the retirement. No routine for me anymore."

Grabbing her purse and keys in an attempt to move away from the topic, she replied, "I tell you what, I have to go and prepare breakfast for old Mr. and Mrs. Johnson and then get them to their doctor appointments. After that, I must read to the toddlers at the church. Then I am all yours, and we can continue talking. I'll tell you about the dream I had last night while we have lunch. You should find it quite the topic for conversation between us."

THE ADOPTION

THERE ARE NOT A lot of things to make you wake up and continue to be excited with your life's journey. But the idea of love alone is worth the trip. One taste of it will leave you wanting more. It will make you push through all your fears and faults just to be near it.

It was only by coincidence that Kim met Mary the day she found out she was pregnant. It was a Thursday around one-thirty in the afternoon and there were only three cars in the church parking lot when Kim pulled in and began to cry. Most of the noon-day service members had already left.

Mary locked the large oak doors of the church and headed toward her car when she noticed the young lady crying. She cautiously approached and tapped on the window before asking, "Are you okay?"

Kim was too upset to notice Mary had walked toward her car. She raised her head and looked up from her lap. For some reason Mary's presence somewhat calmed her; perhaps it was Mary's church-mother appearance.

"I didn't think anyone would mind. I only need a minute." Kim spoke.

“You don’t have to be in a rush. You are more than welcome to stay as long as you like. Do you want to come inside? The pastor is still here.”

“Thank you, Ma’am! I do not need the pastor, but can you sit with me for a minute? I don’t want to be alone right now.”

An hour quickly passed as Mary and Kim sat in the parking lot of the church. Mary listened as Kim cried and slowly divulged the bitter parts of her life and her newfound pregnancy. An unexpected friendship developed that day and Mary and Kim’s lives would be inextricably entwined forever.

Kim had been on her feet all day tending to the affairs that needed her attention, and she was exhausted. Her ankles burned as she shuffled up the driveway at six and a half months pregnant; it was beginning to steal her energy. Her pregnancy bump had been showing for a while now, and her glowing fair skin made her a beautiful mother-to-be.

After leaving the doctor, she drove across town to meet Mary. It was a routine they had started shortly after making their agreement. They exchanged greetings and smiles.

“How do you like the name Kennedy? I just know this baby is going to be a girl.”

Mary laughed, her cheeks glowing with excitement. “That’s a beautiful name!”

“I just thought of it on the drive over, after listening to an interview with Jackie Kennedy on the radio. But I must tell you, Mary, my mind has been racing all week long.” Kim’s voice was shaking. “We are going to need an attorney, and how do I tell Phillip I’m giving his baby up for adoption? This town is going to have a lot to say. My mother is so upset with me. People are going to lose their minds.” All this came spilling out in a single breath.

Mary’s smile got bigger. “You have to relax. We control the things that we can.” Her wise words were comforting to Kim.

“Let’s try to get as much of this done today.”

"Have you told your husband about Phillip and the baby?" Mary asked.

"No! Even though he has given me my space, I did tell him there is something we need to talk about. I did tell him I met someone that I occasionally spend time with. But, to answer your question, I have not told him I am pregnant. He would hit the roof! How do I tell my husband, who I have not seen in months, that I'm six and a half months pregnant? And on top of that tell him and Phillip I am contemplating adoption? I just don't know how to do that."

Placing her hands on her swollen stomach she began to rub and speak to it. "Kid, you're going to do amazing things because right now this is absolutely crazy!"

"Maybe you don't have to tell your husband unless there's some urgent reason to do so."

"I couldn't do that. We may be separated, but I don't feel it would be right not to tell him that his wife is pregnant by another man. Oh, just saying it makes me feel horrible. What have I done?"

Mary put her arm around Kim and tried to comfort her. "It will all work out. You'll see." She steered the conversation back to the subject of the visit.

"I have given this so much thought," said Kim. "As you know, my mother is in no position to raise a child. She could barely talk about my relationship with Phillip. When I told her I'd had an affair, it devastated her. And the fact that I'm giving up the baby! She fell apart when I told her. It was as though I'd committed one sin after another, piling insult onto injury. No, that angle is completely off the table. She made that clear the night I told her about the affair. Now that I'm thinking about it, she didn't seem to be too surprised; her only response was, 'Tell me about him. I need to know all about the person who's so important you would risk your family."

The remark had startled Kim, and from that point forward her mother had wanted nothing to do with her and Phillip's relationship. But Kim couldn't believe her mother would forsake her own grandchild, regardless of Kim's involvement with another man.

"Mary, this baby will not be raised in Mississippi, and I still have every intention of trying to save my marriage. What I am trying to say is that you're the only person I know who has a stable life. So, I would like to take your offer.

Mary appeared shocked as Kim continued.

"I only have three requests of you and your husband, Earl." Holding her fingers up, she began. "One, you give this baby everything that I can't. Two, I have six months to change my mind, and three, she must know who her biological parents are. And I'm going to need to bond with her in order for me to heal. I'll leave all the other particulars to you."

Mary's eyes lit up. "Absolutely! Of course! I'm so excited about the arrangements and feel truly blessed that God has given me a chance to be a mother. I have prayed for this for so long. Earl and I have wanted a child our entire marriage; we were close to giving up. For years I imagined what it would be like raising children; the things I would teach them! Would I be a good parent and mother? I'm just engulfed in emotions right know. You know, it was not too long ago the Lord spoke to me in a dream. His words made me sit right up. 'Get ready' is what He said, and it scared me to death. It is all making sense now, even the way we met. Oh my God, I'm not even sure why I asked you about adopting your baby when you told me you were pregnant."

Mary was all smiles. "I just blurted it out without thinking and it definitely wasn't nice. I must have sounded like a fool."

Dipping a tea bag into a cup of hot water, Kim echoed, "Well, I wasn't planning on meeting Phillip, having another baby, or giving a baby up for adoption. The Lord moves in strange ways, as you know, if you can even make the claim any of this is the work of the Lord."

Kim sighed before continuing. "You know, I came to Florida to visit my mother and to get myself healthy so I can return to my family. Now I am pregnant with Phillip's child, and my life is spinning out of control. How can I fix this mess that I have made?"

Mary spoke softly, "Sometimes we have a tough time living our lives from a place of comfort. Perhaps it's because of the unknown."

She leaned forward to comfort Kim, unsure of what her next actions should be. They stared at each other, the air between them filled with emotion. All they could do was hold hands and cry.

Mary wiped both of their tears away with a handkerchief and softly whispered, "I'm going to pray. Heavenly Father, I come in prayer with Kim asking for your forgiveness of the sins we have committed against you and your Holy name. We ask for forgiveness for our loved ones as well. Father, you came so that we may have life and have it to the fullness of your glory. Father we know that you don't make mistakes and even if we don't understand this pregnancy, we know that it is your will. So, we come right now, Father, asking that you break every curse. Remove any generational curses that lay in our bloodlines. In the mighty name of Jesus, we ask that you break any generational strongholds that hinder us from receiving your glory. Father, we ask that none of our sins be passed to Kennedy; keep her and protect her. Heavenly Father, we ask that your angels be released to watch over her; may they go before this child so that she may walk in abundance. We pray that she may live without fear, we pray that she does not have to live with the boundaries and struggles that Kim and I face. We pray, Heavenly Father, that there is and always will be an anointing on her life in the mighty name of Jesus. May you turn your face toward us, Father, and smile upon us. In Jesus name. Amen."

Kennedy and Greyson sat nuzzled together on the outdoor shower bench. He noticed the water on her face was not coming from the shower. They were tears slowly streaming down her face.

"Honey, what's wrong?" Greyson wiped her tears with his thumb.

"I know I've told you I was adopted, but I'm a little overwhelmed thinking about it. My life could have taken any direction for any number of reasons. My mom–my adoptive mom Mary--used to tell me there was a blessing and angels over my life and I used to think it was her just being the super-Christian mom. There have been so many angels, Greyson. So many that I sometimes forget they were ever there. My life could have been so different. I have held onto so much of this for far too long. Wow! She was right." Kennedy held her face in her hands.

"It's all good, babe. With everything you are preparing for tonight with your award, it must be stirring up some things about your past. Keep talking. I'm all ears." He held her and made her comfortable so she could share more.

THEY HAVE TO PAY

PHILLIP PACED BACK AND forth, unable to control his agitated movements. The walls seemed to be closing in on him every second that passed. The anger and betrayal boiled as he tried to gather his rage and emotions. "I need a drink," he growled under his breath.

The sudden news of Kim giving the baby up for adoption made him livid. "This is my child, and she has no right to do what she's doing without my consent." He was alone, but he beat the argument from both sides. "How dare she!" A photo of him and Kim taped to the fridge had him stuck, so much so that he had forgotten why he entered the kitchen. The photo was of happier times with Kim. He studied her hair and face in the photo; her beauty still calmed him.

Phillip desperately tried pushing his anger aside. "She won't get away with it. I know—we're not married. Maybe I have no rights. But a baby! Surely that gives me some rights!"

Opening the fridge door, he grabbed a beer and slammed it on the counter behind him. The images of a pregnant Kim flashed in his mind bringing back his rage. The same kind of rage that chaperoned him the three days he sat in that foxhole in Vietnam. He thought that part of his life was behind him, but Phillip was a dangerous man, a time bomb waiting for the right circumstances to set it off.

Leaning on the counter with both hands, he began to ball his hands into fists. He wanted to smash something, then he remembered there was whiskey in the cabinet underneath the counter. Without hesitation, he retrieved the bottle and began to pour himself a large glass of Wild Turkey.

"Why the hell is she going to give my child up for adoption?" He screamed into the air. "That's my child! She doesn't know who she is messing with." He pointed his finger as if someone were taking part in the conversation with him.

His shirt caught the corner of a chair and he angrily ripped it off. He paced frantically around the room. A moment later, he blew out a deep breath in another attempt to pull himself together. Phillip knew it would take everything he had and all the anger management techniques that he had learned in order to cage the beast that lay within him. Reaching for his drink, he gulped down the liquor and felt the smooth burn it created in his throat.

"This is crazy as hell! This isn't working. I've got to talk her out of this. I want my child!"

He soon realized that the alcohol and breathing techniques were failing to ease his pain—the torment he was unable to control. Phillip rushed to the back room returning with his Smith & Wesson 38. He poured himself another glass of Wild Turkey and the dark liquid overflowed the glass, just like his anger was pouring out over everything he knew now, but he did not care. He continued to pour even as the liquid puddled onto the floor. He threw the bottle against the wall, shattering it, then crashed down into his chair and began to rub the pistol.

"Fuck these bitches! I'll make every one of them pay."

DISAPPEARED

"FUCK THESE BITCHES! I'LL make them pay."

Phillip meant every one of the seven words. The thought of taking revenge calmed and focused him, and gave him a sense of being in control, of having power. Power! That's what Phillip was all about. Being in control. He gave no thought to regulating his own actions. What he wanted was control over others. He wanted respect, whether it was deserved or not. He wanted people to look up to him, to admire and revere him. And if that didn't happen, he had no problem taking it by force. He had a king's complex.

He would be patient as to how and when he would take action on them. He gave no thought to consequences or outcomes.

"Collateral damage," he mumbled to no one, as he pictured his intended victims begging for his mercy. But there would be no mercy. He would see to that. He wanted everyone to suffer the way he was suffering. He wanted everyone to know that he had power. He would take what he wanted the same way he overpowered, intimidated and took what he wanted from his father's gambling customers.

Kim had been warned about Phillip's anger by everyone she met who knew him. The entire town felt he was a privileged, unaccountable adult that most women had learned to stay clear of regardless of how handsome he was. And even though she had not been the recipient of his anger, she knew that a whole town could not be exaggerating about his temper. Phillip was the bad boy by every definition of the word when it came to women. Kim was unclear about whether she simply enjoyed the thrill and excitement of the forbidden or if, at some point, she thought she could change him. But as the saying goes, "you can't change a tiger's stripes."

Their relationship had not been a bad one, but there were a few red flags over the sixteen months of what was clearly an affair. They had produced a child together, yet it wasn't enough to make her want to continue the relationship with him. And she knew she couldn't continue to live in the small town, especially if she was giving the child up for adoption. Her mind was made up; she was determined to return to Mississippi and repair her marriage.

That decision was made as she lay on the birthing table bringing Kennedy into the world. She looked at Mary who was holding her hand. She knew she had made the right decision and that God had put her and Mary together at the right time and in the right place. Keeping Kennedy would only serve as a constant reminder to her and Edward that she had had an illicit affair that had produced a child. She didn't regret having the child, only the way in which she had received it. But she tried to remember that life's path has many twists, and for Mary's sake, she knew that the path she had traveled—the one that led her to Phillip and ultimately to Kennedy and Mary—was a matter of divine intervention. She knew it was right however wrong logic made it seem.

The placenta passed from her body after Kennedy's tiny little body slid from her womb, and Kim cried louder than the baby. Mary held her hand tighter allowing her to release all the pain and stress she had bottled up over the course of the past year—Phillip, Edward, her marriage, her mother, the baby, abandoning her children—all the decisions, right or wrong, that led to this moment. All of it.

When the placenta passed, things suddenly became so clear to her. She wanted to start new—a fresh life with the family she already had. She wanted to be a better woman, wife, and mother. She wanted to be the kind of woman, like Mary, who could comfort someone else who was going through a tough time. She wanted to stop running from her race, her skin color, her identity, and start confronting her demons so she could live from a whole and complete place. That was the only way. Why hadn't she seen it sooner? Before she got into this mess. But delivering Kennedy was a good thing. She did not consider the final outcome to be negative, even though the circumstances surrounding the event might have been.

And she also knew that this was not the end. There would still be a price to pay. And she would pay it without reservation, knowing that she had made these decisions of her own free will. Now the consequences were hers to deal with. She didn't know what they would be, but she was ready to once again face the world with strength and courage, and with the friendship of Mary by her side to act as a mentor and guide during the tough times that were surely ahead of her.

The direction of her life was once again clear to her. She was okay with being a black woman, a black wife, and a black mother regardless of how white she looked or what she thought could be gained from her appearance. Two people were born that day: the baby Kennedy and a new Kim.

Shortly after Kennedy's birth and the completion of the adoption, Kim quietly disappeared from town. Mary was delighted in her new role as a mother, but Phillip was furious. He would have his revenge.

"That bitch will not get away from me," he vowed.

Kim's disappearance led her back to Mississippi to try and reconcile with her husband. His forgiveness would not come easy. She prayed that her actions had not torn them too far apart; she prayed that her conquering her depression, postpartum and the birth of a child had not been too much. But she was prepared for his rejection. She had prepared herself in case he no longer wanted his wife and the mother of their children around. The hope of being the girl of his dreams was all she held on to; hopefully, it would be the one thing that could give the marriage a chance.

All the meetings and conversations with Mary during her pregnancy had taught Kim to have faith. No matter how bad the situation, regardless how dire things appeared, faith was the one thing that Kim now had. Her faith told her that Kennedy, the daughter she had given up for adoption, would have a good life. Her faith gave her peace that her decision to return to Mississippi to put her life back together with Edward and her family was the correct one.

Things were rough in the beginning. She had hurt him to his core. When she would try to talk with him, he gave her the cold shoulder. It was brutal for Kim and, she suspected, even more brutal for him. She felt alone in her own home. He continued in his routine of letting his mother take care of the kids and he went about his business as though she were not even there.

The days turned into weeks and the weeks turned into months, and still things did not get easier for the couple. Their breakthrough came one day when Edward came home from work. It had been a long day for him, judging by the worn look on his face. Kim saw the strong crease between his eyebrows which was a sign he was stressed. As he walked in, she greeted him at the door like she had been doing since she returned. But this day was different. He took her hand in his this time instead of passing her by, leaving her empty and alone--abandoned. She felt the pain he must have felt all those long months without her in his home, in his arms, at his side. Devastatingly alone.

"Sit down. Let me help you relax." Kim sat on the floor in front of Edward and began removing his shoes. She got a basin, filled it with water and Epsom salt, and brought it over to him. She gently placed his feet one by one into the warm water.

He sighed so loud the kids came peeking around the corner. She shooed them away. As he slouched down and rested his head on the back of the couch, she walked behind him to massage his neck and shoulders.

"Forgive me, Edward. In trying to find myself, I almost lost you and the kids," she sighed almost as loud as he had. "You didn't have to let me back in after all I've done to hurt you and this family. You are a good man, Edward. More than I deserve."

She walked back in front of him and knelt at his feet. "Please forgive me, baby. I never meant to hurt you or the kids. I was foolish, ignorant and selfish. I love you so much. I just did not know what was happening to me. I..." Kim didn't get to finish.

Edward sat up straight. He lifted her chin with his finger and looked her in the eyes. "You hurt me and the kids more than you'll ever know. There is nothing you can do to take back all you did. But what's done is done." He took her hands in his. "But I forgive you because I love you."

Edward loved Kim more than all his emotion; he had waited this long for her return. In spite of her leaving him with five children to raise for over a year on his own and returning after giving a child up for adoption - a child that was conceived out of adultery--he still loved and needed her. Their love was enough. It appeared that despite all that they had endured, they would make it. Things had become visibly clear that Kim's postpartum depression, leaving her family and having an affair was not enough to destroy her marriage.

A month had gone by since their breakthrough moment, and everything had been going so much better for their family. Edward left for work that day with a skip in his step. But the joy Edward had that morning and afternoon ended once he returned home at the end of the workday. All the kids were in their rooms, and Kim was usually home at this time of day, at the door to greet him. But Kim was nowhere to be found. Nothing was out of place, other than Kim not being home.

"Where's your mother?" he asked their oldest son, who was doing his homework at the kitchen table.

The boy looked up. "She left shortly after we got home from school. Some man came to the door, and she left soon after he did," he said.

"What man? What did he look like?" Edward was now angry and a bit worried.

"I couldn't get a good look at him, Daddy. I was in my room and heard his voice getting loud. By the time I came out, he was gone."

His heart raced with fear, not with the idea of her leaving like before. This was a different type of fear; it was the fear that something was wrong. Kim had won back Edward's trust. She assured him that she would tell him if there was ever going to be changes to her day or changes to her heart. His hands began to shake as he reached for the phone to report a missing person. Edward wondered what the police might think.

"They're going to think she has run off again," he spoke aloud as he picked up the phone. But he did not let that thought keep him from making the call.

Everyone in the small Mississippi town knew of Kim's leaving her family, so it was certain that they would think that she had done it again. They did not know that she had changed, that she was determined to make her family and marriage succeed.

It was seven o'clock in the morning when the police knocked at the door. Edward had not slept one moment since calling them the previous evening. He had sat in the living room chair with the curtains open staring out the window with the hope that Kim would return, safe and unscathed. He had positioned himself with a clear vantage point to see the entire street in both directions, so he was very much aware when the cops turned onto his street. He prayed they were just passing through as they slowly drove up the street in the direction of his house.

Edward tried not to panic when the car stopped in front of his home. He hoped their presence was only a well-being check. He opened the door with the anticipation of saying he and his family were okay. He even started to say the words when he was interrupted. The officers delivered the news that no one wanted to receive. Kim was dead. Her body had been found on the train tracks just outside of town.

"Dead! What do you mean dead? What? How?" he cried.

Edward was grateful the kids were not home. He became overcome with fear as the officer told him the circumstances in which they'd found her and their suspicions about what might have happened to her. He called his dad asking him to pick up the kids. He rode in the police car to the coroner's office to identify Kim's body. In disbelief he stared at the body and looked over toward the sheriff and the coroner giving a quick nod to confirm that it was indeed Kim, the love of his life. The woman who had won his heart in high school. The woman who crushed his spirit when she left him. The woman who returned to him in a prayer and renewed her vows, declaring her undying devotion and love for him. Once again, his life was changed in a matter of a day.

The tears fell from his face as he stared at Kim's body on the coroner's table. He could not believe the direction in which his life had so quickly turned, a knife's edge that cut him to the very heart of all he believed and wanted.

"Edward, I'm sorry for your loss. Forgive me, but I must ask you some questions. You stated that when you got home from work your wife was not there and the children were there alone?"

"That's correct, Sheriff."

"Well I'm going to need to speak with you further. Your wife's death appears suspicious, Edward. There's bruising to her neck, but we will know more once the coroner completes his autopsy."

"Sheriff, my son said that she was upset after a man came to the door. They say they'd never seen him before, but he was angry. They heard raised voices." Edward wiped a single tear that fell from his eye.

"That's good information to know. Okay, I'll be in touch with you. Again, I'm so sorry for your loss. I know what you've been through recently."

Mary quietly sat in the last row in the church desperately trying not to bring attention to herself. On the front row sat Edward, his parents, and five children all dressed in black.

The small church was half full for Kim's funeral. Some of the people cried and others stared aimlessly around the congregation attempting not to join in with the crying. It was not long before the pastor had said his fill; he had succeeded in shouting the crowd into a crying frenzy. It was a scene right out of the Southern Baptist funeral handbook. That repetitive, unimaginative format where the preacher gives a topic, has the congregation turn to a chapter in the Bible, read a few verses followed by thirty minutes of shouting that's unrelated to the topic, only to somehow end it where he started.

Edward and his family stood in the reception line at the church entrance, in the lobby, patiently greeting and thanking everyone as they exited the church. He was numb with grief.

Halfway through, he noticed Mary sitting off to the side of the last bench. Once the line ceased and everyone had left the church, he slowly approached her, rubbing his sweaty palms against the crease of his black slacks as he tried not to appear nervous.

"Mary, it's my pleasure to finally meet you." His voice was soft and low and trembled with his sorrow. He extended his hand toward her.

"The pleasure is mine. My condolences to you and your family." Mary held back tears in vain, for she had become very fond of the young woman who had become her friend and the angel through which God had delivered His promise to her.

Edward could feel the tears starting to fill his eyes simply from their introduction. He had not shed a single tear during the sermon yet here he was, close to letting himself break down at the sight of Mary. He gathered himself just in time; he could see his mother rapidly approaching from the lobby where his dad and the kids waited. Without hesitation he positioned himself between Mary and his mother, shielding Mary from any questions his mother was sure to have for her.

"Edward, darling, please don't be much longer. The children are getting restless."

"I will be along with you guys in a few minutes." He took both her hands in his, a mother's sorrow for her child's pain evident on her face. "Would you mind getting the kids into the car, Mother? Thank you. I just need a few more minutes."

Once his mother retreated, he turned his attention back to Mary.

"I now understand why Kim did the things she did, and I think I'm okay with that. I even understand why she chose you to raise her child. If you are anything like she said you are, I will not contest the adoption. I will keep my promise to her."

"Edward, Kim wanted the kids to know their sister so I'm hoping that we can arrange for them to spend the summers together."

With that being said, Mary placed her arms around Edward holding him tight. Mary's motherly comfort caused Edward to finally break down into tears. Whatever emotion he had previously been able to control came rushing out. Through his tears he whispered, "I love and miss her so much."

LOGICAL FALLACY

WITH THE HELP OF Edward's and his eldest son's interviews, it was not long before the Mississippi authorities notified the Florida authorities and had them question Phillip about Kim's death. The police investigation continued for months with Phillip being their primary suspect. As much as the police tried to link Phillip to the death, they simply could not produce enough evidence even though he could not prove where he was during the time of her death. He had no alibi, but lack of an alibi does not constitute a crime. In this case, Phillip had a reputation that was well-known by Florida state and local police, but because the kids did not see the face of the man who visited Kim that day and could not describe him, once again Phillip was free to continue with his life. Everyone in the small Florida town believed that Phillip was guilty of killing Kim; they all thought he had finally done it and told the police so. But opinions didn't matter. There was nothing to link him to the crime.

His family did not support him through it at all. The old man had finally had enough with his son, and the town made it clear that no one wanted him in it. In Phillip's eyes, Kim was the woman of his dreams and his soul mate. Phillip never admitted to killing Kim. When asked, he only confessed his love for her.

Feeling ostracized now by his peers, the townspeople, his father and everyone who had formerly associated with him, Phillip decided to leave town. Miami was just the place he needed to be to clear his mind of Kim's death.

Shortly after arriving in Miami, Phillip met and fell for a woman who reminded him of Kim. He never shared much with this woman about his past or his relationship with Kim. He never mentioned that her appearance was shockingly close to Kim's. She was the same size and height as Kim, and she also had deep hazel eyes. The only difference between the two was that Kim appeared white though she was half black and half white, and this woman was white.

After his affair with Kim, he loved the idea of dating a white woman. He had seen the way other black men looked and responded when Kim was on his arm. The idea of them staring because of his reputation never occurred to him. Phillip's king complex generally influenced almost all decisions he made and blurred his mind to any reality around him.

Once the opportunity presented itself, he jumped on it. Dating a white woman made Phillip extremely arrogant and even more self-righteous. After his discharge from the military, Phillip had become spoiled and rebellious, and it got worse once he started dating this woman.

He was so used to getting his own way and doing his own thing that it got in the way of his new relationship. When this relationship did not work out, he should have walked away. Frustrations were high and regular, and instead of pulling back and walking away, Phillip's anger overtook him once again as it had many times before. During an argument, he tried to strangle her. Fortunately, she managed to escape before he could kill her.

Phillip no longer cared about anything or anyone but himself, and even that was questionable. He moved through life with a death wish and a vengeance that dulled his senses. Kim was the one person who calmed the anger that usually filled him, and now that she was gone, he figured why not let it all out. It had not been a year since Kennedy's birth, Kim's death and him being questioned for it, yet here he was sitting across from the cops again.

This time there was no good 'ole boy system in place to protect him or cover up his behavior. His aunt, Queen, was a bit of a fixer in her community, respected, and even feared in many ways, by local residents who were in her sphere. But this time she could not save her favorite nephew from the attempted murder charge. Her money and back channel dealings bore no power in Miami and it was even clearer when he was not given bail. Things became evident to Phillip that none of the lifelines that he had access to would be available to him now. He was in a new city with pending charges of attempted murder. Attempted murder of a white woman in the 1970s, no less. And he was without his usual safety net—Queen.

The day of the trial Phillip was prepared for the worst. He sat patiently staring forward most of the day. It was all a formality as far as Phillip was concerned. His anger blinded him to the hurt and fear he had placed upon the woman he harmed. It blinded him to all the people who had attempted to help and save him prior to this moment. All the times his father tried to steer him in the right direction were forgotten along with his own guilt. As far as he was concerned his actions were justified. In his warped mind he thought that she had it coming, and this was enough.

Phillip sat in the courtroom alone during his trial; his rage had brought him to this moment. No family support and no one to advocate for him. And this lack of support did not go unrecognized by the jury or the judge. When it was all said and done, Phillip was given a ten-year sentence with the possibility of parole in five years if he could control his behavior.

Phillip left the courtroom without so much as a glance back. His life forever changed once the gavel landed. Whatever hatred, rage and anger he previously controlled was released at that moment never to be contained or governed again.

"I feel sick to my stomach every time I even think about Phillip." I lifted my head from Greyson's shoulder. "Kim's careless actions led her to that sicko. I think about all the poor decisions she made in life. Her desperate need to take care of herself actually put her in harm's way costing her the very life she was trying to rebuild."

Greyson stared at the tears spilling from her eyes. A small smile crept onto his lips.

"What are you smiling at?"

"You! I'm smiling at you because, considering all of the poor decisions Kim made, there was one decision she made that gave me you." He held my hand. "The decision that gave you life."

Raindrops quickly came down hard as we finished up in the outdoor shower. We both knew it was one of those five-minute rain showers Florida was known for, the kind that would end just as quickly as it had begun. I gave up any attempt of protecting my hair from the damage of the rain. Any other time I would have freaked out and ran into the house at the first sign of rain. But today I did not have a care in the world. I was too caught up in telling Greyson my story and, like I said before, nothing was going to ruin my day. Not even my hair, which was now soaked and sticking to my back and face. In a few hours a stylist would be arriving to repair whatever damage the weather was serving.

I just parted the shiny straight brown hair that was now slightly curly and pulled it behind my ears so that I could continue to stare into Greyson's eyes.

Greyson stood there in disbelief as the shower and rain drenched us from head to toe. "We are really doing this? You are not going to push me aside and make a dash for the house Kennedy?"

"Nope." I took two steps backward so that I was completely under the shower head again allowing him to see the water dance off my naked body.

A few minutes passed before the rain stopped and we stepped from the shower. Neither of us bothered to dry ourselves as we walked through the small puddles on the pool deck. The splendor of the sun warmed us as we silently contemplated the story I'd just related.

Once we reached the covered veranda, I took a seat between his legs and lay back onto his chest on one of the dry cushions. Springing to my feet I retrieved a bottle of Veuve Clicquot from the outdoor mini-fridge and grabbed two champagne glasses. Thumbing through the playlist on my phone I settled on Tanto Tempo, a peaceful bossa nova mix by the great Babel Gilberto. Just as I filled the second glass, two peacocks landed in the yard, startling me enough to overfill the second glass.

The peacocks were from the neighborhood, yet no one seemed to know who owned the flock of beautiful birds that had grown to about seven over the last couple of years. Greyson and I sipped champagne and watched the birds hunt lizards. The sudden rain had stirred up the reptiles causing them to scamper across the deck and foliage.

One of the birds patiently waited for the lizards to emerge from their camouflaged hiding spots. He intentionally narrowed his broad green chest, kept his crown low and made sure to keep his tail feathers tucked into their two-foot train. The second was obviously younger; his feathers had a less colorful tint to them. He chased everything that moved, and he constantly fanned his tail feathers showing the elaborate blue and green eye pattern.

Greyson and I both wondered if the older peacock was teaching the younger bird how to hunt and when to strut to ensure his dominance of the flocks. Watching the beautiful birds somehow reminded me of my young adult life. Their interaction reminded me of the people that prepared me for the next phases of my life.

We both wrapped up in a towel and I nuzzled deeply into Greyson's chest.

"I'm grateful Kim gave me up to Mary and Earl. I would hate to think what my life would have been like if she kept me and stayed with Phillip." A frown laced my forehead.

"Mary and Earl gave me a beautiful life, one filled with joy and comfort. Phillip tried through words and actions, even getting Queen caught up in his schemes, to take all of that away when I was growing up. I never wanted any part of him, and the further away he stayed from me the better I like it."

THE VISIT

"I LEARNED AT A YOUNG age that Phillip St. James had become a killer. After he was discharged from the military, he had been in either jail for small time theft or harassment, or in prison for assaulting or killing women, all charges that were eventually dropped or he had his sentence reduced thanks to Queen." Kennedy continued unfolding the painful parts of her life as Greyson listened on.

By definition, a serial killer is a person who has murdered three or more people, but there must be a certain amount of time between the murders, or it is considered a killing spree. Well, that definition did not matter very much to Phillip.

"People questioned why he wasn't serving a life sentence or at least one which was sufficiently long. The belief was that until he tried to kill that white lady in Miami, he was only hurting black women, and it was a time when the justice system could not have cared less about black people let alone a black woman. Plus, Phillip had the right connections. Queen being his biggest one."

Phillip never received long sentences for his crimes because of a wealthy relative, Queen, who loved him dearly. To her, all his prior offences did not matter. She was there, coming to his rescue when he tried to kill two girlfriends prior to Kim; both times she helped to get the charges reduced to assault. She was there for him when he was arrested for fighting over a woman. He beat that charge by claiming self-defense. She was even prepared to help him when he was being investigated for Kim's death. Her loyalty to him was astounding, but nothing she did could save or help him once he attacked that white woman.

Queen was a woman of wealth and power, and her friends were the good 'ole boys. She was a very light skinned woman with freckles. Her long legs featured under a very curvy body and large breasts. She was drop dead gorgeous with a charming Southern personality, both of which kept people hanging on every word she spoke. She was the woman everyone noticed when she entered the room.

She owned a cleaning service that sent beautiful young women out to clean the homes of the very wealthy. The wives of her clients usually despised the beautiful black women coming into their homes to clean, but their husbands loved the idea of it. Not only did the husbands love it, but they demanded it, so the wives always gave in to their wealthy husbands' requests.

Queen never asked her employees to sleep with a client, but when she discovered that they were intimate she made sure to get as much information as possible. This was one of the ways she continued to be surrounded by wealth and political power. This was her way of having favor when she needed it. Her preacher husband could not have known the full depth of her business, otherwise he may have been ostracized from the church. But Queen managed to extract information from her house cleaners that she kept tucked in her little black book. She would make future use of that information in the form of favors.

Queen was Phillip's aunt, and he was her favorite person in the world. Whenever he committed a crime, she was the person to pay his attorney fees. Oftentimes she would go behind his father's back to do so. She would make sure that she hired the best attorney to keep him from going to jail or to have the sentence reduced.

In the 50s, 60s and 70s, the surrounding cities and counties were controlled by a few families: the McMillans, the Bransons, and the

Overtons. If you wanted a license for something it typically went through one of them. Judges only made it to the bench or the ballot with their approval. Mayors and governors even understood their place in this Florida good 'ole boy system, and if you didn't play the game by their rules, you didn't stand a chance.

At first appearance, you would think they were just citrus farmers and cattlemen, but after a closer look, the power and wealth became apparent. They did not drive fancy cars or wear expensive clothes; it was usually denim overalls and pickup trucks that they preferred. But they owned just as much land as the Mormons.

The good 'ole boys had tailored their business model after Henry Flagler. Flagler was one of the founding owners of Standard Oil. But they were more impressed with the way he had developed and run the Florida East Coast Railway. The same railroad that revolutionized the way commerce was moved through the swamp lands of Florida.

When the turnpike was being built they made sure it passed through their land. The existence of the highway meant people would be traveling. Cars needed gas, and all of it would be purchased from them. They even made sure the entire fuel pipeline that supplied all southern Florida went through their land. Need fuel - pay. Need a truck stop – pay. Get on the turnpike - pay, get off the turnpike - pay, want to put up a billboard - pay, traveling north – pay, traveling south – pay, sheriff - pay, mayor - pay, governor - pay. Queen positioned herself directly into all that power. She had every intention of using it for the advancement of her family. And here was Phillip screwing things up simply because he could not control his temper and his ego.

I was never sure of the kind of blood that flowed within my veins. Had he passed the genetic imprint of a murderer into me, and would I suddenly discover this one day? I sometimes imagined waking up one morning to discover that I had killed someone the night before. These kinds of thoughts flooded my mind and the thought of the person I could become frightened me.

Growing up was particularly challenging because I was often reminded by someone in the town what he had done. And I am certain he would continue to kill if he had the opportunity.

I think I was about six years old the first time I met my biological father. I do not have any memory of meeting him before that age. I am not sure who had the bright idea to take me to a prison. Given my age, all I could think of was playing and the treat of taking a day trip. Surely there would be ice cream and anything else I wanted. I later learned that my contact with him was a planned condition of my adoption.

But this day, Queen had deceived my mother, Mary, into thinking she wanted to spend a day with me so that my mother could have a break. Off we went to meet Phillip in deception.

"Stop, Kennedy! Sit still, Kennedy. You better not get that dress dirty," was all I heard the whole way there. I held Aunt Queen's hand as we walked up to an ominous gray building in what seemed like the middle of nowhere. There was nothing for miles surrounding the building. All I could think of was wanting to leave. But Queen explained that we were here to meet my father. I was curious and afraid at the same time.

"I don't know him. Can we leave?" I asked, only to be given a stern look as she held my hand a little firmer. We passed through security—all very frightening and intimidating for a six-year-old—where men and women in uniforms like police and with guns at their hips, led us through and we were placed in a large room with other people. Families sat at tables talking, kids played. I remember thinking that place must be where adults went to hang out.

After sitting there for what seemed like forever, in walked Phillip, my biological father--the killer. He walked over and greeted Queen before kneeling to introduce himself to me.

"Hi Kennedy, you are so pretty. I like your dress," he whispered calmly. "May I give you a hug?"

I do not know if I was afraid or not interested, but I just stood there staring at him.

Phillip picked me up and gave me a hug before kissing me on my cheek. My little legs dangled as he held me there and my heart felt like it was going to jump out of my chest, it was beating so fast.

He put me down and held my hand as he talked to my aunt. They talked for what seemed like hours. Occasionally he would look down at me and smile. "My sweet baby, Kennedy, you are so pretty," he would say.

Staring at my small hand in his large palm, my mind began to wander, and before I knew it, I shouted, "I want to go home. I don't know you!" Queen gave me a piercing look, but by then I was sick of her, and that disdain has lasted to this day.

The lurking guard soon interrupted the conversation and my fidgeting.

"Phillip," you have another visitor.

Standing behind the guard stood Phillip's latest girlfriend, Sheila. She stepped forward toward Phillip with a huge smile and they embraced for a long time as Queen looked at them in disbelief. Sheila was an old girlfriend of Phillip's who never wanted the relationship to end. She was all too thrilled when he reached out to her from prison.

The three of them talked about his weekend pass and how he would get to spend more time with them and the things that they would do. I was really bored; there was nothing there to hold a six-year-old's attention, and the fact that I did not even know the person I was there to visit made it worse. I had not really been paying any mind to the grownups' conversation, so I was quickly brought to attention when suddenly Phillip and Sheila began arguing.

Two guards quickly rushed over as other guards began to frantically remove everyone else from the large room. People shouted and cursed as the guards tried to take control of the room. Phillip was furious. He lunged and swung his arms as he tried to get to Sheila, but the guards surrounded him and were like a wall of protection, blocking him from getting at Sheila or anyone else.

Phillip shouted, "Let me go you punk motherfuckers. Get your goddamn hands off me!"

In a matter of moments, Phillip's calm had turned into an uncontrolled rage. "You crackers don't know who y'all fucking with."

Sheila was scared. I remember looking at her and her eyes were really wide. She was breathing really hard and hugging herself.

"Bitch, when I get my work release pass, I'm going to kill you." There was venom in his words and a kind of confidence that I now know was a combination of false bravado and psychopathic rage.

Sheila stood there frozen in fear. I stood there frozen in fear. Aunt Queen looked at Phillip with disdain, knowing now that all the efforts she had put forth to protect him had been in vain. She had called in favors. She had used up much of her political capital, wasted it on this nephew she once loved. She now saw him for what he really was.

During my childhood, and what I had heard about him, I often thought he enjoyed his chosen life of hurting and killing women.

When we left the prison, I questioned Aunt Queen.

"Why doesn't he just go home? Who wouldn't want to go home?"

She told me that you could not go home when you wanted to if you lived there. And you had to behave. Phillip had not "behaved", she said, and he would have to stay there even longer now. It made me wonder, at six, if I had behaved well enough to stay out of that place. Regardless, I would be on my best behavior now, I thought.

A killer is exactly what he is, and I do not think I'm wrong to feel that way. He boldly flaunted his actions, describing and embellishing them to anyone who would listen. How could someone be so proud of taking a life?

I had often wondered if he did it to intimidate people or to gain control over others. I guess in many ways it worked, but at what price? I saw the price he was paying.

BEST DAY EVER

I REMEMBER BEING OVERWHELMED BY the whole ordeal of visiting Phillip in prison. Queen commanded me not to tell my parents about any of it, especially not about Sheila and what happened between her and Phillip. But at six years old, the first thing I wanted to do was tell my mother.

"It was so scary, Mommy," I lay my head on my mother's lap. "Phillip was mean to this lady named Sheila. He said he was going to kill her."

"What are you saying, child? Who is Sheila? Where was your Aunt Queen?" My mother hit me with so many questions at once.

"She was a lady who came to see him like Aunt Queen and I did. He was nice at first; I think he liked her. Then he got mad at her." My mother rubbed my head as I shared the whole sordid visit with her.

That night, I heard my mother, Mary, and her husband, my adoptive dad, talking in their room. My daddy made it clear that I would not be going anywhere near Queen, Phillip or that prison again. He said he would die first before he would ever let that happen again.

On Sunday, after leaving church, we drove to the lake just as we did every Sunday to feed the ducks. I was always so excited, and my parents were so patient and caring with me. Mary and Earl loved me unconditionally. Mary worked part-time. Earl was retired from the Army and the railroad. Even though he was almost twenty years older than mom, he was all too eager to be a parent. Having children was the one thing that they could not do together. They adored the task of raising a child even if it meant challenges.

"Kennedy, don't get too close to the water!"

"I won't, Mom! Dad, can we catch one? Please, please." I would beg my dad to let me catch a fish.

"The best day ever! What a beautiful day!" Dad would always say at Sunday dinner after going to the lake. He would take his place in the big chair and I would climb onto his lap. We would tell each other corny jokes until we both fell asleep. Indeed, life was perfect!

As much as my parents tried to make my life normal, things were always a little different from the other kids I knew. And having Phillip as a father did not help.

I always had more than other kids. Was it because they felt some guilt over not being able to conceive? Was it because they were trying to erase the smudge of me having a father like Phillip? I never really knew for sure. But whatever I wanted, I got.

One day, returning home, Dad and I saw the kids in the park playing with their yo-yos. They were doing tricks, twirling them in the air, and it was simply amazing.

I cried and cried, pleaded, and begged for a yo-yo. I just had to be the first in the neighborhood doing tricks with a yo-yo. Off we went to the store in search of the perfect one.

Blue? No!

Red? No!

Red, Green, and Black? No

That is it! A pinkish one with sprinkles of glitter on it. We rushed home with our purchase and things quickly began to fall apart, including my patience and behavior.

As much as we tried, we could not get the thing to do a single trick. Heck, my dad did not know how to yo-yo. He would fling it and it would crash to the ground. I do not think he knew to put the string on his finger.

"Make it work! Do a trick!" I would say to him.

"It's broken! It does not work! Let's take it back! We're taking it back!" Dad was so aggravated.

We must have eventually bought every type of yo-yo at that store. I gave up, and they soon became decorations in my room, decorations that no one could touch. That was how most of my childhood adventures with my parents would end.

A few weeks later, I was at my friend's house playing. The day was as perfect a day as a child could ask for. We played with our dolls, we played hide and seek and any other games that we could think of. The backyard was filled with our laughter. As we played jacks, our game was interrupted by my friend's grandmother.

"Kennedy, Phillip just killed another lady! I heard it on the news. Some lady named Sheila is what they say her name was." She said it with such ease. She delivered the announcement like it was normal or something that was expected.

I wished he weren't my biological father. I never understood why my mother loved me so much and spoiled me beyond belief. But after Sheila's death, I had a lot of questions.

I had a mother, a father, and Phillip. It just was not making any sense to me. We had everything a happy family could have: a home, cars, and money. I had everything a little girl could want, and I loved it; all but Phillip. Why was there a Phillip and why did I know him?

My mother was a very private person. She was super conservative and lived and did everything with discretion and the guidance of the Lord. But when it came to raising me, she would always say, "I will never withhold from you. I will make sure you have everything you need in order to succeed in this life."

I climbed into the bed next to my mom and asked her, "Mom, why did my friend's mom tell me what Philip did?"

She sighed, "Baby, you are going to hear all kinds of things about Phillip, some true and some not. You are not going to like a lot of what you hear, and some people will say things just to hurt you or provoke a response from you. Their words don't require a response."

She looked me in the eyes. "Kennedy, do you understand what I'm saying to you?"

"Yes, ma'am!" Wiping the tears from my eyes we continued to lie there.

"Kennedy, you know how I always say to you that I will never withhold from you?"

"Yes."

"Well, Papa Earl and I tried but we could never have a baby. We prayed and prayed for a baby. It was the only prayer we prayed for a full year and God answered my prayer with you."

With a look of confusion and excitement, I replied,

"Me?"

"Yes! Before you were born, I met a beautiful young lady named Kim who lived close to the other house we had. Kim was pregnant and we arranged for me and Papa Earl to adopt you once you were born." Springing up from the bed she rushed to the closet, reaching deep into the back of the top shelf. She found what she was looking for, holding a folder of adoption papers high in the air.

"I promised her that I would give you a good life, Kennedy. A life with no boundaries. A life where you saw the world differently than the black folks in this town was used to." My mom smiled as she touched the papers. "Kim, your biological mom, agreed, with the understanding that she and your biological father would have a relationship with you. But Phillip did not like that Kim allowed Papa Earl and me to adopt you. He was—and still is--very upset over that.

"Even though nothing has been confirmed, we believe he did hurt Sheila and Kim. I know this may be difficult or you may not understand completely, but I love you more than life itself."

Just as Mary began to cry, Earl entered the room. "Why are my girls crying?"

Falling into the bed, he scooped both of us into his arms squeezing us tightly, kissing us as he whispered, "Best day ever! What a beautiful day!" Every time he said that it made everything feel better.

DAMN YOU PHILLIP

My mother used to give me so much information and advice. But most times she would only have half of my attention or I simply did not want to hear it. Then there would be those times when what she was saying would stop me in my tracks and never leave me. This was one of them. I do not recall how old I was, but I do remember being in my room listening to music. She walked into my room and turned everything off. My mother was never forceful about anything. However, this day she took me by my face and held it firmly.

"Kennedy look at me! Every day that you get up, the devil has already been awake waiting for you. When you have an anointing on you, which you have, he knows it and he will use everything in his power to keep that anointing from you. The devil does not fight fair. He will use your friends, your family, your career and your faith to try and shy you away from your calling." She kept her grip tight on my face. "Kennedy, you have to know that you're in a battle, and when you don't know what is possible you will settle for what is available."

It was one of the most powerful things my mother ever told me.

"There she is! There is my precious girl!"

The sight of my broad, snaggletooth smile did wonders for Earl's morning. My grin widened as the sound of my make-believe big-girl heels clicked on the hard wood floors. Taking my place on his lap, I lay my head on his chest. Leaning in I planted a kiss on his cheek, the rasp of his beard tickling my nose making me smile. "Papa, your heart is beating fast!"

Rubbing his chin, Papa Earl pretended not to hear my comment and said, "Momma needs to give me a shave. Don't you think so?"

"I can do it," I said.

"She is the only one that can shave me, maybe she can teach you someday."

"What about when I get bigger?" Kennedy reached up and scratched at the bristly beard. "It's sticky."

At that moment, everything was perfect in my young life. Philip was really nonexistent. But there were always subtle and not so subtle reminders of him everywhere. People in the small town thought it was appropriate to remind me that my father was a killer.

But my home was a safe space that always put me at ease. Home was the perfect protection. It was a fortress of love.

Momma started singing one of her favorite songs, "Hallelujah", the one about David playing a secret chord for the Lord. She used to sing that song to me every night.

"Earl! Kennedy!" Mary called from the kitchen, "Breakfast is ready!"

"I think we should hurry along." Papa rubbed my hair lifting me off his lap. With big smiles on our faces, we quickly took our places at the table.

"Pancakes are my favorite! Yours are the best, Momma!"

Mary smiled softly and returned to making our plates and cleaning the counter and stove in a single multitasking motion. All those years of perfecting cooking and house cleaning were finally paying off.

"My family is finally complete," Mary whispered and smiled as she watched us from the kitchen, humming her song.

"No elbows on the table when you eat, Kennedy! That's not proper table manners!"

"Yes, ma'am!"

Mary turned her attention too Earl. "Earl, are you okay?"

He shrugged, "I think I have a little heartburn. I was hoping to spend the whole day with my girls; the three of us don't spend enough time together you know."

"Well you are welcome to join us, Earl. I must sign Kennedy up for dance classes and I must take the cakes over to the church. But you can't rush us."

"If that is the only rule, then it's settled. I am yours all day. We can have lunch at that new barbeque place across town. I hear it's rather good, and they got ice cream." Winking his eye at me.

Looking at me, Mary chimed in. "No manners, no ice cream!"

I quickly removed my elbows from the table and looked away as if no one saw me or nothing happened.

"If you are done, you may be excused from the table to get dressed." Wasting no time, I thrust a "Thank you ma'am" over my shoulder and rushed to my room.

Mary laughed. "Make sure you wash your face and hands," she called.

I was so excited that day. I jumped and danced on the bed when I reached my room, performing my dance moves for my teddy bears and other stuffed animals.

And then there was an earsplitting scream from the kitchen. I jumped from the bed and flew down the stairs. I could see Papa lying on the floor.

"Momma, what's wrong with Papa?"

"I don't know baby! Go back to your room!"

I did as I was told, mounting each stair slowly, looking back, frightened by something I didn't understand. From my room, I could hear the sirens approaching the house. Sitting on the bed, bending over my legs and holding my socks, attempting to make a circle that afforded some kind of comfort, I could hear the voices of the paramedics in the kitchen.

"Dear God, please let Papa be okay. I promise to be a good girl," I prayed.

Several minutes later, Momma entered my room, her eyes red rimmed from crying.

"Don't cry, baby. Everything is going to be alright. Papa is going to be okay. Let's get your shoes on. We have to hurry to the hospital."

Sitting in the waiting room, surrounded by beige walls and the patter of staff going up and down the halls, Momma held my tiny hand tightly. Words failed us for what seemed like an eternity as we stared straight ahead, unblinking, an occasional tear slipping out of momma's eyes. Every so often we would look at each other, try to squeeze out a smile and return to looking at those beige walls.

"Momma, here comes the doctor!" We stood, anticipating his words.

I hung closely to Momma's side with both arms wrapped around her as the doctor delivered the news of Papa's passing. Their attempts to save him had failed, though they did everything they could, he said. The doctor was polite and professional. Papa Earl was gone.

"Momma, no! I want my papa!" The words got choked in my throat and died on a whimper. Momma had collapsed into the chair and I broke down crying in my mother's lap. My prayers to God did not work.

To this day I have never had, nor will I ever have, beige walls in my home, no matter how popular the color might become.

Later that evening, I clung to my mother's every move as all the family and guests visited to console us. They talked about how devoted Papa was to his wife, Mary, and about his twenty plus years to the A & A railroad. They spoke of how people respected him and how proud he was to be a father.

After all the guests had gone, Momma prepared the bath for me. She stared at the wastebasket in the bathroom in an attempt to distract herself from the fact that Earl was gone. As she mindlessly studied the basket, she noticed a crumbled-up letter sitting at the top of the normal items of bathroom use.

Reaching into the basket, she quickly noticed that it was sent from a prison. She nervously unraveled the letter, only to find a few haunting threatening words.

"I'm going to kill you and your wife. That is my daughter."

Momma began to cry as she rushed to her room trying not to alarm me. "Damn!" she yelled with her face buried in the pillow. The soft-spoken Christian had never cursed before. However, this time she just could not hold the emotions in. Laying there crying, she must have wondered if that letter was the only one. And if it has caused Papa Earl's heart attack. Jumping to her feet, she quickly dismantled the closet in a whirl of flying clothes and shoes, but she did not find a single letter. Frustrated, she turned her attention to the dresser.

I had quickly dried myself and followed her from the bath. I didn't want to be alone—without Momma—for even a minute.

"There has to be more!" she whispered as I watched her through the crack in the open door.

One by one she went through the drawers, only to find some used undershirts neatly folded in the back of the last drawer. She would have never noticed them, but they did not bend when she picked them up. Momma's nerves began to boil. She retrieved the packet and fell to her knees, the carefully hidden letters in her hands. As she read their threatening words, she could not believe Papa Earl was able to keep them from her for so long. Every letter mentioned Phillip planning to escape prison so he could come and kill my parents.

"Earl why? Why wouldn't you tell me?" She cried out as she looked up at the ceiling.

Phillip had claimed another victim…my Papa.

NEXT

I WAS RAISED IN A black family in a black neighborhood in the South. However, if you were to travel the country and visit any black community you would find the same rules of behavior and discipline in just about every home. I am sure you have heard a comedian tell a story or joke about your parent telling you to go get a switch or being beat with a belt or extension cord. In most cases, that joke was very much true.

I recall an incident several years ago at a Walmart. A child was having a tantrum in the store with his mother. He was out of control. After several unsuccessful attempts to gain control of the child, the mother spanked him in the store. Once the spanking ended, the child's tantrum stopped, and they finished their shopping. But not before she gave him that other prominent often heard warning, "Wait 'til I tell your dad," which usually meant bigger problems for you. The child's father spanked him again at the car. The entire incident had been witnessed by several people, but one person filmed it and called the cops.

The local news got the story along with the video footage and it became a major story. White people lost their minds; it was insane. The parents were arrested, and I am sure the Department of Children and Families got involved.

Most black people were confused. They did not see any problem with the public discipline. To them, it was like that parent was saying,

"I'm going to get your butt in this here Walmart parking lot while you're a child so that you're not on a dash cam video later getting beat by the police."

So, go get me a switch....

Thinking back on my life and losing my Papa at such an early age made me think about what I missed by not having a father around to help raise me, teach me how to be treated as a woman, and discipline me so that I didn't go astray in life. Would my life be any different had Papa Earl still been around for the later parts of my life? I guess I'll never know. But it does make me think about how I was raised versus what I see in today's society.

After my father died, it took a while before my mom and I adjusted to not having him with us. But slowly we began to build the life that we wanted. I know raising me on her own was not easy, but she never complained. She simply found a solution for whatever we faced. Surprisingly, never once did she say she was a single parent; she always included my father as if he was still there parenting even after his passing.

Most of the other kids were being told, "Wait 'til your dad gets home," or some other threat about their dad. I, on the other hand, constantly heard, "What would your father think, Kennedy? Would your father approve, Kennedy?" Her courage was incredible.

My mom had a home built for us on the other side of town. I often wondered if my father's death in the other house was something she was trying to escape, as though it was a continuous reminder of his heart attack. I would sometimes see her hiding her tears when we lived there. It seemed everything reminded her of him.

Once we moved, things began to improve; we had a new home and began a new life. Not only did our lives improve emotionally but financially as well. My mother developed an entrepreneurial spirit, probably out of a lack of something else to do, like taking care of her husband. I'm sure she only did it to keep herself active and occupied so that she wouldn't focus on Papa's death. She opened a home health care services agency. It was an opportunity that arose when some of her elderly friends who were blind began to need help with their daily living. It was not long before she had a staff, and I could see that light of joy returning to my mother.

Shortly after the success of her health care agency, she opened a cleaning service for private families. Thinking about it, all my mother's business ventures were things she was already doing. One day she simply got smart and turned her passion into licensed businesses.

My mother was a fifth-grade dropout from a small town in Louisiana, but what she lacked in formal education she made up for in the study of faith, human behavior and life. She managed those businesses with the rule of integrity; she concentrated on treating people with respect. With the success of the business, the rental of our first home and my father's retirement pension, money was never an issue for us.

I loved my new home and new neighborhood. It was like moving to a new city. Our new neighbors were a large family. I loved spending time with them even though the parents were big on discipline. There was a vast difference between their parenting style and my mom's. I got away with everything (within reason), but if the neighbor's kids did anything wrong, they were met with the belt. Bad grades - go get the belt! Come in the house and not speak - go get the belt! I was shocked at the number of rules they had to obey and the discipline that followed if they stepped out of line.

"Don't make me get that ass," their father would always say. I was terrified of him; yet for some odd reason I loved being at their home regardless of how terrifying I found their father. Their mother, on the other hand, was a very sweet lady. She was the kind of lady who would hold you and console you when you fell off your bike and scraped your knee. If the other kids made fun of you or were too harsh to you, she would come up with something to make you feel better, like a home-baked cookie or a piece of licorice. When all else failed, she would present a cup of hot cocoa with tiny marshmallows and whipped cream. (I confess I sometimes shed crocodile tears a little longer hoping to get that antidote, and I suspect she knew my ploy all along.) And she was the best cook in town. That alone was enough to make you keep showing up.

In my younger years, we would stay out all day playing. We would smell like outside or be covered in dirt, yet she would always make us stop and take a break for lunch or dinner. Sometimes it would be both. And it would not be a sandwich or something simple; it would be fried chicken, pork chops, rice, and gravy.

In middle school we would go to the football or basketball games every Friday, or we would go to other community events like the annual fair at the church. On Sundays, we went to church without fail. Their church was a much larger church than my mother's sanctified church. There were lots of kids my age there and the church had fun activities for the kids. The church would take us skating in the big city, to water parks and the beach. We had so much fun. It was nothing like sitting on the back row shaking a tambourine at my mom's church.

During middle school, I quickly learned that I was the only one in my group participating in activities. I had begun to travel all over the county participating in parades and performing in local shows. After finding something that I genuinely enjoyed, I began to shed some of my mischievous behaviors.

This was a blessing to my mother because throughout elementary school I had behavioral issues. Not the kind that required medication or the need to be placed in a special class. I just did not like following rules, or I just did things to get a reaction, like standing at my desk instead of sitting in it to do my work. I would stand there the whole day. Who knew that I was simply ahead of my time since that's a thing now—ergonomic workstations--people working at their desk while standing?

Much of it stemmed from losing Papa, but I did wonder if it was in my DNA. I was assigned a behavior coach to help teach me problem solving the correct way. We met after school for an hour twice a week. She gave my mom assignments that were designed to help me stay focused, but after a while she told my mom that she needed to punish me. She didn't say how, but she said I should be made to accept the consequences of my actions, that my mom needed to set clear boundaries with penalties for breaking them.

However, my mom was extremely optimistic when it came to me. Through it all, she never gave up on me, she was very patient. She had made a promise to my biological mother, Kim, and she was determined to keep it. She had also vowed to make sure I knew Kim's children from her husband, Edward. My mother had kept in touch with Edward after Kim's funeral. She would check on him from time to time.

After Kim passed, Edward had raised my siblings with the help of one of their aunts, but he never fully recovered from Kim's death; a part of him died with her. Edward nearly lost everything after her passing, including his children. The house which they now lived in was a loving home, but they did not have much money. Seven people lived in a small three-bedroom house, and both Edward and their aunt worked all the time to support those kids. They did their best with limited resources and skills. Mary sent Edward money from time to time to help, and my sister and brothers never complained about their circumstances. Having each other was more than enough.

Every other year, my mother would arrange for them to spend the summer with us. I loved it when they came to visit. We used to have this huge canopy oak tree in our front yard. It was the spot where all the kids from the neighborhood came to hang out. Maybe it was because of the swing that hung from one of the branches, but it was the spot to be. My sister and brothers loved that swing; we would spend the whole day laughing and playing under it, taking turns swinging and pushing. We would see who could go the highest, then we would launch ourselves from it to see how far we could fly. It was like our very own summer camp.

Mom would make lunch for every kid playing under that tree - sandwiches and chips - but our favorites were the ice cream and the watermelon. And we could always count on my brother, Jonny, to have watermelon juice all over his face and a shirt that was soaking wet when he finished. The days that we did not have ice cream or watermelon, we would hope and pray that the ice cream man would come by. The days that he did not come, we would walk to the store and buy candy. I remember walking to that store two or three times a day.

By the time we reached middle school age, all the girls had a crush on Eric, my older brother. Eric could really dance, and the other girls ate it up. He would dance and skate with them at the skating rink then he would be off to battle someone in a dance contest. At one point, people from all the surrounding cities would come to battle him.

I cherished the summers they came because I was the only kid from the neighborhood who was an only child, everyone else had a brother or sister, and it was my turn to finally say "my brother" or "my sister."

When they visited, I was always on my best behavior. I did not want them to see me as a bad kid, a spoiled child who had more things than they did. I was kind and considerate to them because my mother made sure I understood how differently they were growing up than I was.

Mary was a woman of strong faith who believed deeply in God. She prayed for me while I was in my mother's womb and I believe that God covered me in the blood of Jesus, and a covenant of an anointing was placed on my life. She shared with me one of the prayers she prayed while I was in Kim's womb.

> *"Dear God, I thank you for this beautiful child. May she grow up covered by your hedge of protection. Keep her from harm's way and grant her peace all the days of her life."*

She prayed for me before she officially became my mom and throughout her entire life.

My mom had some prominent friends, and she would always get advice from them and try creative ways for me to become successful at controlling my behavior. I was placed in almost every activity or sport there was. There were swimming lessons, soccer, basketball, dance, baton twirling, and piano lessons. I was active in anything that she believed would help me curtail my sometimes erratic and irresponsible behavior. All her hard work and efforts were starting to pay off as witnessed by my better behavior and my interest in safe healthy activities.

I rarely told her anymore about the comments that continued to occasionally come my way. "Your father is a murderer." For me, participating in these activities helped curtail my need to lash out and redirected any thoughts of Phillip away from me.

It was not until Mary found dance and baton twirling that things really began to change dramatically for me. I must admit, I was pretty good at both. I could sense the movement of the baton as I heaved it into the air and envision where I wanted it to go, the exact impact it would make when it hit my hand coming down; I could somehow exaggerate every dance move, sometimes feeling like a bird in flight, just like the birds I used to watch out my window when I was a child. I remember thinking back then that if I could only decipher their song, I, too, would be able to fly. It was a very fanciful and naïve thought, but here I was, sailing across the dancefloor, coming up with my own routines, and feeling stronger and more confident than I ever had before. I was so good that I knew I wanted to be in the marching band when I got to high school. My goal was to become a majorette.

HAPPY BY DEFAULT

Band had made a difference in my behavior. I began to care more about my academics and the way I treated people, probably because I was treated better because of my position in the band. Or at least that's how I felt. I guess you can say I was finally starting to grow up, but I still had moments of acting like a spoiled brat.

Halfway through middle school I noticed that some of my friends were getting boyfriends or they were starting to take interest in boys. But I noticed none of the boys liked me nor did I like any of them. I think I was too skinny and much smaller than all my friends.

All the girls were developing faster than I was, but at the time I was simply happy with wearing the best clothing and having much more than everyone else. I was on an ego trip for sure, but it really didn't matter that some boy did not like me because I had dance recitals and baton competitions that took a lot of my time.

At the time, I did not mind being the only girl without a boyfriend. But what I did mind was what my friends were saying. They would say the girls with the biggest breasts would get the most guys. There I was, a skinny kid with no breasts, and self-conscious about my body. Little did I realize at the time that all that dancing would develop me into a very attractive lady.

Something I did notice was that the boys talking to my friends were not in middle school; they were in high school. This did not make sense to me, neither did I understand how they kept contact with these older guys because they did not go to school with us nor did they ride the bus with us.

Other than my neighbors, most of my middle school friends lived in an apartment complex, so they had the opportunity to see and meet all types of people. One day, my neighbor explained how it all worked. The guys would have a conversation with them and tell them how pretty they were, then they would begin to write letters to one another, and it wouldn't be long before the girl became crazy about the boy, mistaking lust for love on his part.

One time, my friend was talking about what a great kisser a particular guy was. I did not want to believe that she was sneaking away kissing an older guy. A few weeks later, she announced that she was not a virgin anymore. Shortly after, I noticed that she no longer liked that guy but had a new boyfriend.

I also had another friend who lived in the same apartment complex. The same guy that had sex with my first friend also liked this other friend. Months later, the same guy pulled the same trick on another one of our friends. She wanted to have sex with him for the first time, too. Well, this same guy had sex with four of my friends within the space of six months.

The crazy part was they all would talk about it like it was nothing. I thought that was the stupidest thing ever and questioned how these girls could be so dumb. I already knew that I would not fall victim to a guy like that, the way my friends had.

One day I went to visit them in the apartment complex And there he was--the guy who took the virginity of my four friends. As I was walking on the sidewalk in his direction, he smiled as I approached. I was already known as a brat, and there was the "her daddy is a killer" reputation I had in the neighborhood. So, I knew he was simply out to prove a point or make a name for himself at my expense.

As I walked by him, I rolled my eyes and put my nose in the air. I whispered, "Jerk!" under my breath just loud enough for him to hear it, hoping to make him feel ashamed of what he had done.

As I got closer, he said, "Kennedy, you think you're all that. You are no different than these other lil hoes around here."

He tried to get up in my face and I sidestepped him. Without hesitation I grabbed a rock from the ground and threw it, striking him in the center of his forehead. I ran away fast, and I turned to see him stumbling around and cursing. But I did not care, nor did I care what anyone else had to say about it either. I just continued walking to my friends' apartments with a smirk of satisfaction on my face.

"I *am* all that and more," I said to myself, smiling.

After that day, I realized that it was better for me to spend more time with my neighbors and stay clear of the apartments. The neighbors' conversations revolved around more diverse topics than just sex and guys. They were in high school and I was younger, but they still took me under their wings. They taught me how the neighborhood worked, who to avoid, and to never take crap from anyone. Even when their parents divorced and they moved to another house six blocks away, I would go to their house almost every day. I was like family to them at that point and they to me.

Their new house was in a larger subdivision and when I went over to visit them, it did not take long before I was introduced to more people from their new neighborhood. Everybody knew each other, and we would walk everywhere together. More people were added into our circle and that is when I met Rodney.

Rodney was comical--a nice guy who was also known for telling great stories that kept us laughing. He would keep us amused for hours with his stories. We knew most of them were highly embellished tales, maybe even outright lies, but they were entertaining, nonetheless. Over the summer break, Rodney and I built a friendship that, over time, developed into having stronger, more romantic feelings for each.

We would spend time together all day long, laughing and talking with each other during the summer months. He would offer to buy candy and snacks during the day. However, money did not mean much to me. I always had everything, so I looked at it as a kind and gentlemanly gesture. We would catch the bus to the big city to do our school shopping. I did not want my mom taking us and neither one of us was old enough to drive. Not everyone had the opportunity to shop in the big city for school clothes. However, every year my mother and I traveled to Orlando to shop. And I would not have it any other way.

"I love shopping in Orlando, Momma! None of the other kids get to stay on top of the latest fashion trends like I do." I smiled and shrugged my shoulders as I did a little dance move and held up a hot pink polo-type shirt with a pleated mini denim skirt.

"Don't go getting the big head, Kennedy. I buy you nice things because I didn't always get to have nice things growing up." Momma took the mini skirt out of my hands and placed it back on the rack. She smiled at me as she replaced it with a denim skirt that went below my knees.

I tried to stay ahead of the fashion trends, and I would almost always be the first one in my town to wear the latest styles. I think I was envied by most of my peers even when I didn't try to make them feel that way. But it felt like I had paid a big price to finally feel good about myself, so I did not care what others thought of me and my fashion. I was the same girl, only I was reaching for different things and I had a mother who would give me anything I wanted.

Rodney was the perfect first boyfriend. He was goofy and funny, which was all a girl my age wanted back then. Even though I no longer acted out in anger, I was still a spoiled teen who wanted to have everything her way. We would spend most of our days studying - at least he did. If I had difficult classes, my mom would hire tutors to help me so I better understood how to do the work, or they would work with me so I could effectively write my papers.

I went to Rodney's house two times a week, while my mom was in church, all because I was "afraid to be home alone." I am sure he thought I was clingy, but a kiss was all that Rodney really wanted when we were together, even if I was clinging.

To be honest, once the sun went down, I would be consumed with fear. Fear of being alone. I really did not like being alone. It had been that way ever since Papa Earl died.

JANICE COOPER AKA "THE JET"

When I was about eight years old, our neighborhood was like most neighborhoods. We had a candy lady, and she was usually someone's mom or grandmother who sold Winn Dixie Check sodas, pickles, candy, and flips, or what some might call frozen cups. It was nothing for us to go to the candy lady several times a day. Going to the candy lady was the joy of our hot summer days.

The problem with the candy lady was the uncertainty. You never knew when she was open or when she was going to run out of things, and then there was the issue of selections. If you wanted a Coke or Pepsi, she didn't have it, so you had to get that grocery store-brand cola. "I don't have that!" or "Come back in a couple of hours; they're not ready yet." It was so annoying.

"It's Florida, it's one hundred degrees outside. You knew we were coming! Why aren't the flips ready?" We all yelled the same thing at the same time in varying versions as we stood outside her door. Here she was doing something nice for us, but we had the attitude now. Every day we would swear to not go back, but that boycott would end just as quickly as we spoke it.

However, we never allowed these obstacles to stop us. We just changed our plans and walked to the store, which was a couple of miles away, so we could get what we needed. But on our way home from the store, it always turned into a race back to the house. I hated losing and being last; they would make fun of me because I was younger and smaller, and I could not keep up.

"Kennedy, you can't go with us if you can't keep up. You better learn to run fast," my friends would say.

As much as I hated losing, I was more afraid of being left alone, and when you are much smaller than all the other kids, it's even more terrifying.

"You better keep up Kennedy. Someone is going to get you!" they would say.

The fear of someone 'getting me' was always on my mind during those flip and store runs, but the thing that frightened me the most was the thought of the neighborhood pitbull chasing me. This animal was nothing like the dog, Petey, from the *Little Rascals*. There was no sharing your ice cream and friendly snuggles with this dog.

I had witnessed how that dog would chase kids, only for the kids to be saved by jumping to the safety of the hood of someone's car. That dog would have them stranded on the top of cars for hours. I swear that dog was evil, and it would appear from anywhere and everywhere; in fact, I do not even know who owned this beast.

So, I learned to run…fast.

The first year of high school was great; things continued to go well, and everything was great with my boyfriend, Rodney. I was still involved in dance and baton, and I became the first black majorette in the high school band. I even started taking piano lessons again, which led to me playing for the church's Sunday school program, with pay. This was something new for me. Could I actually get paid for doing something I liked doing? Was it possible to earn income from something like dancing?

It was a constant challenge to find time for my friends with my new schedule, but we made the most of our time at school. By now, they had each gone through several boyfriends and had sex with different guys. I loved hearing erotic stories about their sex lives. Even though I was still a virgin, I found their stories very entertaining. I don't know that I really grasped all of it, but they were my girls and we supported each other in everything. I was there for them after every one of their breakups. They would come and support my performances and cheer the loudest for me at pep rallies and games.

Later in the school year I made the track team. I only tried out because one of my friends was joining, and after a little training, I became good at the hurdles. Once again, I was flying. Track was something new for me, but I had always liked trying new things and mastering new challenges. I was really driven and focused on the track, like I had a purpose, and the results were starting to show - I was no longer the skinny kid who could not keep up, but a strong competitive young woman who was beginning to take herself seriously.

I began to impress at the local and regional meets. Things were great. One by one, Saturday after Saturday, I would not just win - I would dominate. The wins came easily... and then I started hearing the name "The Jet." Janice Cooper, aka "The Jet", was from a high school in Orlando. Her school was known for producing four- and five-star athletes in every sport.

Janice was currently the state champion in the hurdles. It was a title she had held onto since middle school, and the nickname, "The Jet," was not a misnomer. The girl was fast. Real fast.

I admit the first time I saw her run I was intimidated. She made it look effortless. Janice devoured every opponent she faced on the track. She was like a boxing heavyweight champion in his prime. She crushed her competition. Most were beaten before they ever stepped into the blocks, defeated in their mind, limiting their ability to really give the race an honest go; they ran only to see who would come in second or just how far they could run before they lost.

She had obviously heard of me because, after her heat, she stared at me without saying a word. She smiled, and with that smile I knew I had a chance. But I knew within myself that it would take everything I had to defeat her. I tried not to give our battle much thought. We were scheduled to compete at a conference a few weeks out, but it was all everyone wanted to talk about.

"Kennedy, did you see Janice's times today?"

"No!"

"Well, we heard that she was calling you out."

"Listen guys. Janice can do whatever she likes."

"We know you aren't going to let her talk trash. She is obviously calling you out, Kennedy. You better represent."

"Why are you guys trying to start something? I thought y'all were my teammates?" I was exasperated. "You know I haven't even been running track for a year. I do not even know my full potential yet, and here y'all go trying to push me to do something I may or may not even be capable of doing! What is it you want me to do? What do you want me to do? Fight her, curse her out, or race?" I was anxious to hear what they would say.

My teammates stood there, silently assessing me. They had no response to what I said, or so it seemed. Then I heard someone yell, "She's scared!"

I was in disbelief; this was nothing like dance or baton competitions. These girls wanted me to *do* something. I was frustrated and I had had enough; I grabbed my bag and started to walk away only to stop again and give them a piece of my mind.

"One more thing. I don't even know what I'm doing out there. Right now I am just having fun, but I guess I'm not supposed to have fun! But I'm the one about to race the state champ, not you—any of you. So much for being a team you guys. Why don't you just come out and support me? We can take it from there and I'll let you decide whether or not I'm scared. I mean, after all, I not getting into the ring with Muhammad Ali."

"She's scared!" I heard someone whisper again, and they chuckled as I walked away.

With everything going on, at least I still had my boyfriend. I had finally given in and had sex for the first time. It was a much different experience than the ones my girlfriends described. We had fallen in love, and it was a great connection. We saw each other every day at school. My evenings were filled with activities and track practice, but we still created time for each other every Thursday night because my mom went to church on Thursdays. My mom would take me to his house, his mom would cook dinner for us and we all would watch TV together. I still had the fear of being home alone, so Thursdays were a welcomed reprieve for me.

The day of the conference, the clouds began to gather, and the rain was imminent. I threw myself into a whirlwind of stretches to stay loose after popping two Midol to combat menstrual cramps courtesy of an overnight visit from Mother Nature. I put my headphones on to get into the zone. Getting out of the blocks was going to be the key to my victory if the track became wet that day.

Several minutes passed before I heard Janice Cooper's name being called, along with the other racers, over the loudspeaker. The racers had to go to the starting block for the first heat. Janice quickly put away her opponents, doing just enough to qualify for the finals. Her strategy was obvious; just finish with a win and a good qualifying time. Leave them wondering what more she was capable of. She had an ace in the hole and she obviously wanted to keep it a secret.

It was the same strategy that my coach had developed for my first race, and it worked perfectly right before the sky let loose. In Florida you could set your watch to the afternoon rain. It usually lasted about twenty-five minutes to an hour before the storms would pass through. The sun shined brightly during that day's rainstorm as we took shelter under the bleachers. My concentration continued to be broken by the sound of runners screaming, "The devil is beating his wife." This was something we said as kids when the sun shined during a rainstorm.

A half hour had passed after the storm blew by; the track was still wet when they called us to the starting block. My heart went into overdrive as I placed my first foot onto the block. The excitement could be felt throughout my whole body, my fingers tingled as I blew out a shaky breath and kneeled into the second block. I heard Janice sigh and thought, "Here's my chance!"

The starter pistol rang out, and with a burst of energy I sprung out of the blocks trying to stay in my technique and not think about my step count. I was the first to reach and clear the first hurdle, but Janice was right on my left hip. I could hear her spikes click right after mine. I could not tell how far back the other racers were, but the clicking of Janice's and my spikes tapping the track in unison told me we had the same stride count as we cleared the next eight hurdles. As we approached the final hurdle, I broke the first rule of sprinting: never look over at the competition. My focus was lost and so was the race as I clipped the hurdle and crashed to the track. There was no dramatic fall in slow motion like in the movies. It was sudden and jarring and all I could do was brace myself for the fall. When I got to my feet, a second sprinter passed me and all I could see was Janice crossing the finish line.

I pulled myself up and went on to cross the finish line. I stood there in disbelief, catching my breath and looking at the scrapes to my palms and knees. Janice walked over and wrapped her arms around me saying, "I didn't want to win this way. You're pretty good, but don't fall next time."

I walked over to my coach and sat beside him. My hands and knees burned from the road rash, but the pain of losing hurt way more than the missing skin on my hands and knees.

"Way to go, Kennedy! Good job," was all he said before I burst into tears. I wiped away my tears and turned and limped away. "I can't freaking believe I fell."

RUN FOR YOUR LIVES

THE SOUND OF A boat approaching quickly grabbed our attention. We were used to hearing the boats on the lake. After living in the community for so long, we could tell if a boat was getting close by the difference in the way the waves hit the shore. We could distinguish engine sizes and boat types, all something we'd learned from living on the water. Greyson grabbed the two robes that hung next to the shower as our friend Ellis throttled down to drift alongside the dock.

"Da'vee," he shouted, using the nickname he'd spun from our last name, Davenport.

I giggled, hiding behind the shower wall, and quickly slipped into the robe.

"I know y'all home, Da'vee!" he shouted again.

"Man, why are you making all this noise?"

"What's up family? Greyson, I started to run you over out there an hour ago. You better be glad I thought of Kennedy and Kylie!" Ellis laughed. "Good morning, Kennedy!" He leaped from the boat holding a bottle of wine.

Ellis looked as if he had not slept, and he surely didn't care about his appearance. He wore a pair of Gucci house slippers, board shorts slung low on his hips and an unbuttoned dress shirt with cuff links. He was unconventional for sure, and a true friend—he was the dog that fought to the end—a person you wanted on your side should you ever find yourself in trouble.

"Good morning, Ellis! It looks like you're in a good mood this morning."

"Well you're not the only one who has something to celebrate. Let's just say my day is off to a great start."

Dropping to one knee as if he were proposing, or more like an Englishman presenting the queen a gift, he bowed his head and extended the bottle toward me.

"Thank you, Ellis. You may now rise."

"Hey, I would love to hang around here and drink champagne, but I have a date to get back to. I just wanted to say good luck tonight and bring you this *very expensive* bottle."

Greyson smiled at Ellis in disbelief. "Man, you mean to tell me you left a woman at your house just to bring that bottle of wine over here?"

"Y'all are family," he shouted from the boat. "Plus, this just gave her time to snoop through my things!" He slammed the throttle forward sending rooster tails fifteen feet behind the boat, his shirt billowing in the wind, and we could still hear him laughing as he disappeared up the channel.

Ellis lived a few nautical miles away, at the other end of the lake. I had met him several years earlier when we shared a board seat for the homeless shelter. Ellis and I did some wonderful things on that board; we were great at raising funds for the shelter.

I later introduced him to a girlfriend of mine who only agreed to go on a date with him if Greyson and I went along. That date did not go so well, but a couple of weeks later, Greyson invited him to a Maxim magazine Super Bowl party, and they have been the best of friends ever since.

I was so excited for the new school year; everything started out the same as last year. School, practice, rehearsals, competition, and my boyfriend. But this school year was different because I was turning sixteen in a couple of weeks, which meant I was getting a car, and I was already thinking of the freedom it would provide.

My mom allowed me to have my birthday party at one of the rental properties she owned. At the time, it did not have tenants occupying it. She said she did not want "all those teenaged, hormone-filled kids" wandering around her house, so the rental property would be perfect. We had spent weeks planning it down to the letter.

My birthday party was everything I could have imagined. There were close to seventy-five teenagers scattered throughout every part of the house. We all danced, sang, ate, and danced some more. I must have drunk three to four cups of punch before my cousin told me he had spiked it with vodka.

Even after it was all over and I lay awake in bed that night, I could not stop thinking about it. My ears rang and my head pounded from the loud music, but I could not care less as I lay there smiling. People had come from all over, friends and friends of friends. Every time I tried to fall asleep, a new memory of the party would come to mind and push the sleep away. I could hear Papa Earl's voice saying, "Best day ever."

Since I couldn't sleep, I walked over into my mother's room. I gave her a demure smile as I slid into bed with her. "I can't sleep," I whispered.

"I know. I could hear you laughing from here," she said.

"Mom, thank you for everything. I really love my car. Did you see all their faces?"

They all said I was lucky. They could not believe my mom got me a Camaro Z28 with all the options, including T-tops. I tossed and turned for a while longer, then kissed her.

"You know what helps me fall asleep?" Mom asked. "Singing, Kennedy! Give it a try. You can sing *Hallelujah* with me."

As we lay there singing, I could not help but think about how my new car was nicer than anyone's in town, including my mom's. She loved me so much and she always wanted me to have more than she ever did. I loved and appreciated her more than she would ever know.

Having my own car gave me more independence and freed up some of my time. Before I knew it, the time I spent with Rodney went from little time to just about no time, and he was not happy about it. I was making a lot of new friends. He continuously asked where I was. He even began to accuse me of cheating, and I knew the time had come for us to part.

I waited 'til Thursday after dinner. We stepped outside and I told him I no longer wanted to date him. I knew he would be upset. However, I never thought he would react the way he did.

He grabbed my arm hard. "You're not going anywhere. I'm not letting you go. Why are you doing this to me? Haven't we been good together?"

"It's just time for us to move on, Rodney. I'm sorry," I said.

"But I don't want us to move on, Kennedy." He began to frighten me. His voice was tense and harsh, and he would not let go of my arm.

I pushed him and he pushed me back. I swung and slapped his face. For a moment he looked stunned, then a sort of rage boiled on his face. And that's when he punched me in my stomach. I doubled over, grabbing my gut, shocked at what had just happened.

"I have to go!" I choked out the words and walked away forever. I never spoke to Rodney again.

After the breakup, I enjoyed not having a boyfriend. I never mentioned to my mom about Rodney hitting me; I feared how she would react. But now I was able to do the things I wanted to do and not have to think of someone else's feelings. I was busy and outgoing; my schedule stayed full.

I got my first job with Disney World just a few months before track season began. I thought it would help me be more responsible. Besides, I saw it as an opportunity to meet new people from various places. I loved working at Disney World, and it was there that I met Kelly.

Kelly was from an upper-middle-class family that really enforced higher education. She belonged to Jack and Jill, an organization dedicated to nurturing future black leaders, and one that well-to-do black people put their kids in.

Kelly and I hit it off immediately. She would invite me to their parties and fundraisers where I mingled with other girls, all beautiful and highly intelligent, and guys who seemed to be just as smart, and with a smoothness that I found a bit perplexing. I'd already been exposed to some of the ways guys can sweet talk a girl, but this group was different—it was hard to catch them at their game, if that's what they were playing.

The way I saw it, their lives were no different than mine. They just had more exposure than I did. So, I was determined to not let any of that bother me, but I sure as hell was not going to have them snooping around my life, opening up the possibility of having them find out about Phillip. He was deep in the background, my background, but he was there, a dark secret that seemed to haunt me every time I met someone new.

Kelly was a little different from the other girls from what I could see. She had an edge to her. She was very smart and driven. And she liked sex--a lot, especially with different guys. She dated several guys at one time and slept with every one of them. I once asked her how she was able to do it.

"Look, Kennedy, every one of these guys wants to be my boyfriend, but that's not what I want. I'm just playing the game the way they play it."

"But aren't you worried they will find out about each other?"

"Find out? Girl, I tell them up front so that there's no misunderstanding."

That was her thing, and I did not judge her for it. She was surrounded by cute and well-mannered guys from families of money with dreams of college and success. This appealed to me because they were different from the guys in my town, and because they had the same dreams and aspiration as I did. I had no idea what I wanted to be or do, but I knew that I wanted to leave my small town and become successful. I was not sure how it would happen, and I hadn't given it much thought because I was an average student with limited exposure. But I believed in myself, and I knew something great would come to me even though my life had a sad beginning. However, my life was not a lie or a tragedy despite the grief I had experienced. But everyone experiences grief. It's part of life, and in this sense, I was no different than anyone else. I guess it's how we handle our grief that makes the difference.

Most of the people I'd know—the people I grew up with-- had no ambitions or wanted anything more than what the town offered. They were happy with their small-town mentality, dating the same guys, having babies from the same guys in the same town and working average jobs. I knew I did not want to be a Kelly and I knew for sure I didn't want the proposals of a small town.

Track season was fast approaching. Once the season started and the team began practicing, Coach made me anchor on the relay team, which meant more training. I did not mind. In fact, I welcomed it because between the partying with Kelly, dance performances, baton competitions, and work, all I thought about was beating Janice.

On the day of the Show Walter Preseason Track Trials, I arrived focused. I destroyed the competition in the hurdles. Our relay team also showed good times in the relay heat. Our hard work and focus had placed the team in a great position. This gave us the rest of the meet to ourselves.

Keith had just run his final race for the day, and when he walked over to me, I had completely forgotten that I had met him at a Jack and Jill party with Kelly.

Keith was a pleasant distraction from the long day. All our races for the day were done, so we made the most of our free time, talking and laughing over some of the antics he'd seen at Jack and Jill, with me contributing stories about the locals in my neighborhood. It was a congenial way to unwind. We sat in his car making silly jokes and talking about his plans for college. He told me his parents wanted him to run with the hope of getting a scholarship. Then he offered me a beer from his cooler. I knew I should have declined, but I did not. I tried chewing gum afterwards in an attempt to hide the stench of the two beers I drank, but Coach gave me a look that pierced right through me when I got on the bus. Adults can be scary sometimes. It's like they know everything you're trying to hide from them, like they've done it all long before you did. I don't know if he could smell it or if my eyes were red or if he saw me in the car drinking with Keith, but I knew I was in trouble, and not only with him. It suddenly dawned on me that drinking could interfere with my future performance.

I was nervous as hell sitting in my car before Monday's practice. By the time I got out of the car, the trouble I was facing was so distracting that I did not notice the crowd that had gathered. There seemed to be way more people at the track that afternoon. I kneeled and tied my shoes just as Coach appeared. He pulled me to the side.

"Kennedy, we need to talk. You are off the team," he said.

"What! Why?" I responded.

"I think you know why," he said.

"Tell me why I am off the team," I demanded. I stood there as everyone looked. The crowd grew larger as they began to figure out what was happening. They began to whisper, "She got cut."

"Tell me why I am off the team," my voice grew louder.

"Go home, and I'll call you and your mom later."

But none of his words seemed to matter. I was enraged. Someone from the crowd yelled, "What are you going to do, Kennedy?" Surely, they wanted to add to my frustration.

"Go home, Kennedy. I will call you and your mother tonight."

"To hell with you," I screamed as I headed to my car. My blood boiled with anger. I removed my T-tops and gently placed them in their protective bags. I needed everyone to see me as I climbed in behind the wheel. I slowly removed my shoes before tying the laces of the left and right one together. Once they were tied together, I gently placed the laces around my rearview mirror allowing the shoes to dangle from it.

By now I was seething. Some maniacal demon demanded justice. It was as though I was outside of myself, watching my own actions and having no control over them.

I removed my headband and the scrunchy from my ponytail. I ran my fingers through my hair with deliberate intention. Every move was slow and exaggerated. I was infuriated and about to unleash my wrath. And anyone who happened to be in the way was going to be collateral damage.

"How dare he cut me without telling me why." I did know why, but I wanted to hear it from his mouth, like it would make a difference in his decision. I was infuriated. I'd been schooled in front of a crowd, treated like a child.

"He's going to call my mother? Really?" I started the Z28 and revved the engine, exaggerating my presence, making sure everyone took notice. The RPM indicator went to the red.

"Hey, Coach!" I made sure I had his attention and gave him the finger, then let off the gas and floored it. The car rocketed onto the track. Kids scattered in all directions yelling and running for their lives as I sped around the track. I did several laps at top speed and finished with a couple of donuts in the center of the field. When I looked back, I saw that the infield had been destroyed. The rearview mirror told the story of people cheering, some crying and a coach who was thoroughly angry. Thank God no one was hurt.

And then I thought of Phillip. The killer. Who was this girl who had just torn up the field and endangered the people around it in a maniacal display of pride and ego? I'd essentially just ruined my chances of getting back on the team. A single tear fell from my eye and I took a deep breath. It frightened me to think I could blow up like that, out of control.

On the drive home I obeyed every traffic law. My driving was perfect. I was calm and present, almost contemplative. You would have thought I was a student driver taking their driving exam.

Once I got home, I cleaned all the dirt from the track out of my car, took a shower and went to bed praying my mother wouldn't find out what I had done. But a prank of this magnitude was sure to get around, and fast. She *would* find out.

My emotions had gone from cold to hot back to cold in seconds, I questioned myself and examined my soul as I lay in bed. I knew whose blood coursed through my veins. I'd pulled some tantrums as a kid, but never anything like this. It made me realize I needed to check myself sooner rather than later. It was an eyeopener into my psyche—my behavioral patterns—that I'd never seen in myself before. And it wasn't pretty.

When my mom got the call from the school, let us just say she was not pleased. I went from being kicked off the team to being expelled in a matter of hours.

NEW YORK TIMES AND LONG HAIR

After my complete breakdown on the track and the resulting expulsion, my mother arranged for me to finish school in Ft. Pierce with my aunt, Queen. It pained my mother in every way to do it, but she didn't have any other options. None of the local schools would take me with an expulsion on my record, and financially, it didn't make sense to send me to a private school for such a short time. It was Aunt Queen or nothing.

My mother's back was against the wall and my stupid actions had put her in that position. Plus, there was the deceptive prison visit from years ago she had to take into consideration. In the end, though, she settled on sending me to live with Queen to finish out the school year.

I really believe she wanted to give me a punishment that I would feel—that I would remember. Even though Queen loved me, she sure did not like me very much. I didn't like her either, so our relationship during our time together was one of tolerance more than anything else. I stuck to my studies and extracurricular activities, and she stuck to her commitment to let me stay there—as long as I behaved. Fortunately for me, Aunt Queen's life was a tad on the unconventional side, so what she considered acceptable was a bit different than my mother's idea of the same.

Queen never approved of my adoption; for some reason she felt like her nephew would have been a great parent. She had conveniently forgotten his deteriorating behavior after exiting the military. Maybe it was because of my stern decision in not wanting anything to do with him that had caused her to dislike me. And she definitely didn't like me refusing to call him Dad.

But it was only for a semester and a half, so I did everything I could to make it palatable for both of us. I just needed to get through it so I could move out and move on. And let me tell you, the punishment was received.

I hated the idea of knowing that every day I woke up she was going to roll her eyes during every conversation. Queen was determined to see a relationship formed between Phillip and me, and I was just as determined to stand my ground. Every week I called home complaining about being there, so my mom found activities for me to participate. That way, I would not have to spend a lot of alone time with Aunt Queen. It worked for us both. She was just as happy to have me out doing something so she didn't actually have to converse with me.

After a few shouting matches with my aunt about being late or completely missing school activities, I eventually persuaded my mom to let me have my car.

By the end of the school year I truly had learned my lesson. I was able to go home. The day I left her house was the last time I saw my Aunt Queen. We spoke on the phone from time to time, and still do, though not very often, and to this day I have never taken another step inside her home. I appreciate her having taken me in when I needed her, but I have no intention of reliving her tyranny.

Kelly and the girls from Jack and Jill were so excited to see me when I returned home that summer. All we wanted to do was party. We traveled to Orlando every weekend to hit the clubs. This was our routine over the summer before Kelly left for college.

Every Saturday, we went to a club called NY Times. I was not old enough to get in so I would share an ID with one of my friends. They did not care that I was a junior in high school. In their eyes,

I was cute, I had a car, and I did not have restrictions and curfews. My life was just like theirs.

On the other hand, my friendship with the girls from the neighborhood was changing. Even though I continued to remain close to them, I desired more...more than hanging around that small town could offer. Nothing ever changed with them. They continued dating each other's men and having sex with the same guys. They were living the kind of life that I would never live. But that was their choice, and I guess they were happy with it.

I wanted so much more from life. I wanted to leave certain parts of my past behind me, and living there, hanging with them, was a constant reminder of everything I did *not* want.

My other activities kept me busy. I was usually the only black person participating in certain things, so I tended to attract attention. This gave me the opportunity to meet and make friends with classmates I might never have otherwise associated with. I lived it up with them.

Black kids "go out." White kids "party." When you party with white kids, there is a lot of beer drinking, bonfires and water sports. Other than that, it was not much different than going out with my black friends. They drank beer too, just not as much.

These kids seemed not to worry about how they looked, what they were wearing or what someone else might think. It was all about having a good time; it appeared they were so free with life!

Watching the clock did not help. Time seemed to be at a standstill all day. I had arranged a great New Year's Eve. My date, David, was to pick me up for dinner at six. Then I was meeting the Jack and Jill crew to usher the year in at NY Times.

David had become my boyfriend. This did not go over very well with the black guys at school. Even though none of them liked me, I guess any black girl dating a white guy would have offended their egos.

The first time I saw David was when he was introduced in math class. He was a new transfer from California that sent all the girls into a frenzy. His curly ponytail and west coast accent made him stand out in our small-town school. I mean *all* the girls were after him.

I met David officially on a Saturday when a group of friends invited me to hang out at the lake. I noticed that he had been watching me the entire afternoon, so after a day of boating and waterskiing, we all sat around relaxing and making small talk, and I wasn't surprised when he asked me out. We went for ice cream, had dinners together, and spent many study sessions together.

He was the first guy I dated who was not black. I remember the look on everyone's face when David and I walked into the Cattleman's Steakhouse that New Year's Eve. Between his long hair and the long kisses, we heard a lot of whispers. It might have been inappropriate for us to be kissing at the table. Maybe it was unseemly. Or maybe it was just that we were of different races. I don't know. But we sure raised a lot of eyebrows.

I wore a cute summer dress from Esprit with cowboy boots. I also brought my heels so that all I would have to do was change my shoes after the dinner. David had already made other plans for his after-dinner partying, and at about 10:30, we parted ways with a kiss and a promise to meet up the next day.

It was about ten forty-five at night when I picked up my girls. I slipped on my heels, threw my cowboy boots in the trunk, and was ready for the second part of my evening.

The club was packed when we arrived. There was a line around the building. DJ Magic Mike had the dance floor loaded. People were dancing at their tables and on the stairs.

Magic Mike was an upcoming DJ who had trained under the head DJ at the club. It didn't matter that he was only about sixteen years old and still in high school. He had the gift that would later earn him a Grammy for Best Dance/Electronic Album and was one of only a few DJs to have ever received this award. Magic Mike knew how to keep a party moving.

We must have danced the whole evening, and all we could think about afterward was food. About an hour had passed while we ate at Krystal's, the popular spot to hang out after a night of partying and chatted with a few groups of people. It was after 3am when we finally headed home, exhausted.

I do not remember falling asleep and running my car off the road that night. The highway patrol informed me that it appeared to be totaled, but everyone was okay. We were lucky. He'd seen worse, he said. Because we were all minors under the age of 19, we had to get checked at the hospital. It was about four o'clock in the morning when our parents began arriving. I was sure that as the driver I was going to be in big trouble, but no one yelled. In fact, each parent was relieved to learn we were all okay. Kelly needed a few stitches on her face, but that was about it. Thank God for seatbelts.

To my surprise, my mom just held me and said, "Everything is going to be okay." She rarely got upset about anything. I apologized to the other parents for a month, but each would always give me a long hug and say, "It's okay."

EUPHORIA

BEFORE HIS HITS *1999*, *Little Red Corvette* and *Purple Rain* in the fall of 1981, Prince was not a rock star. He was an unknown with one R&B hit single *I Wanna Be Your Lover*. Mick Jagger was a fan, so he extended an invitation to Prince to be the opening act on the Rolling Stone tour.

The Stones were breaking attendance records and the L.A. Coliseum had close to ninety-four thousand seats filled that day. Prince and his band took the stage, and before a single note was played, it was clear that this was not going to go well. It was his attire: a trench coat, thigh-high boots, and black bikini briefs. The crowd quickly began to hurl racist and homophobic slurs at him and his band. I am sure Prince could take the boos and derogatory remarks, but the food thrown at him and the band was the final straw. It was too much. In the middle of "Uptown," Prince walked off stage and flew home to Minneapolis.

The following day Mick called Prince telling him he had had all types of things thrown at him, and with a little persuasion, Prince was back on stage the following day to finish the tour. But he received the same response throughout the rest of it and vowed to never be the opening act again, regardless of who the headliner artist was.

I fell in love with this story the first time I heard it. All I could think of was how knowing your worth can make all the difference in a life, and how those Stones' fans must feel now knowing they ignored a genius.

No one wants to be the person that misses a genius!

The first time I heard a Prince song was at Skate World. The song was *Head,* and I was hooked. The beat was sick. I did not know the words or what the song was about. I simply liked the beat. It was unlike anything I had heard before. You see, those days you had a simple choice. It was either Michael Jackson or Prince! That song solidified it for me. I was all in on team Prince.

That night was amazing! The lights from the arena pierced the darkness of the evening like a laser show. You could smell the aroma of weed as the Tallahassee Police directed traffic. It did not seem to matter that law enforcement had officers everywhere.

Clouds of smoke floated and burst into the night from all directions. We had taken the roof off my new Pontiac Fiero, so there was no barrier between the smoke and the pulsating music. *Let's go Crazy* and every other Prince song railed from the cars as well as the songs from the B-side.

"I can't freakin' believe we are here. Prince!"

"I know! This is going to be a great show! I'm probably going to be grounded after tonight, Kennedy."

"Don't panic on me, David. Besides, who wouldn't mind being grounded for seeing *Prince*!"

"You're right."

"It wouldn't surprise me to see your parents here. I mean who doesn't like Prince!"

"Well, I don't think that's going to happen. They're parrot heads."

'They're what? What's a parrot head?"

"Jimmy Buffet. Do not tell me you have never heard of Jimmy Buffet! Margaritaville? The parrot on the shoulder?"

"David, we live in a small country town, and I live in a black neighborhood, so, no, I haven't heard of Jimmy Buffet. And what's a parrot head?"

"That's someone that follows Jimmy Buffet. It's like a super fan!"

Once we parked, David took my hand as we walked through the thick froth of people. We darted in and out of the crowd like the game Frogger, trying not to get separated. Occasionally, he would stop only to ask if I was okay. After what seemed like forever, we finally arrived at our seats just as the lights began to go down and Vanity Six appeared on the stage.

The crowd erupted when the lights came up revealing three women with perfect figures in lingerie. Joints volleyed back and forth between the crowds. "Let me hit that" could be heard all around us. I was getting a contact high and laughed every time someone choked or coughed. For some reason I found it funny to watch someone trying to find the air in their lungs once marijuana smoke was mixed with it.

This was not the first time I had been around weed, and it surely didn't bother me that people smoked. Yet, this was the first time I had been around so much of it.

David and I kissed and danced the whole first act. During intermission, we talked about our drive to Tallahassee to get here. It was the farthest I had driven away from home. I had taken day trips to the beach before, but they were only thirty to forty miles away. Tallahassee was something altogether different.

I had lied to my mother, telling her that a cousin and I wanted to go to the Prince concert. I had never deceived my mother before, and I never thought I would have to. But asking her if I could go to a concert in Tallahassee and stay in a hotel with my boyfriend just did not seem like something she would approve of. And if she had found out who I was with, I am sure she would have come searching through the whole concert, weed contact and all, to drag me home. I could just picture her rushing the stage in her church dress.

"Excuse me, Mr. Prince. Move out of my way." I could hear her voice as if she were there. It was like I could even see her snatching the mic from him.

"Kennedy, you have ten minutes to meet me at my car!" Then, turning back to him saying, "You need to put on some clothes young man," before giving the mic back to him. This image stayed with me throughout the rest of the concert and I chuckled each time I saw her in my mind's eye.

"Kennedy, you're crazy!" David choked back the laughter hearing my story of my mom interrupting Prince.

"I'm not kidding, David. My mom would do it! She may even have a couple of women from the church with her!"

"For real? You're joking, right?"

"My mother allows me to get away with a lot of things! And let us just say I have a long leash, but this might prove to be too much."

The sound of *Peter Piper* quickly stole our attention from the conversation. "Kennedy, come dance with me!"

This was our first real date since New Year's Eve, and it was turning out to be amazing. I looked deeply into David's eyes as we danced in the aisles and talked about him moving away. We promised to visit each other and to continue to date.

Dearly Beloved, followed by a guitar intro, echoed from the stage speakers. A blinding white light demanded our attention. Smoke filled the stage and a silhouetted figure with a guitar appeared. The crowd erupted, and women began to scream and faint. Women in camisoles and lingerie rushed the stage as men just stared. Even some of the women who were not wearing lingerie undressed to their bra and panties. They had come to worship at the altar of Prince as if the Holy Ghost had taken them over. Women outnumbered the men in attendance, and it was clear that they were under his spell. For over two hours, Prince controlled the crowd like a puppet master.

"That was the best concert ever." David said back in our hotel room.

"Are your ears ringing?"

"Yea."

We laid across the bed exhausted. David kissed me, but all I could think of was the disappointment my mother would have if she knew where I was. My thoughts turned to the image of her barging into the concert and dragging me home. I don't know if it was the contact high from all the weed, but my paranoia had taken over. The laughter and joy I had been experiencing all night suddenly turned to panic, and just that quickly, I was a mess. Whatever happiness I had prior to the show was now filled with guilt. David and I laid there trying to not think about our deceit or how early we needed to be up. The long drive back home that awaited us was our last thought before falling asleep.

SENIORS

"HEY GUYS, I'M HOME!" Kylie shouted throughout the house. Greyson and I had a sense of relief. If it had been five minutes sooner, Kylie would have found us on the veranda half naked.

"Upstairs in our bedroom, honey," I called out. She entered the room with a huge smile on her face and began to dance.

"It was a unanimous vote, I'm the new chapter president!"

"Congratulations, Kylie!" Greyson and I sang out in unison.

"You two look so happy. What have I missed?"

"Not much. I was just telling your father about the time I met Prince." I tried not to smile and expose the prank I was playing.

"Mom, you never told me you met Prince." Her voice was filled with excitement.

"Sure, I did! Remember I told you about the time me and your Aunt Murphy were in L.A.? You're sure you don't remember?" I continued trying to hold in the laughter.

"I think I would remember something like that. Besides, you suck at pranks, Mom, and I can tell you're up to one right now."

Greyson chimed in, "She is so right, babe. You are horrible at pranks. That was just painful to watch."

"Well, I was there at one of his concerts. That's almost like meeting him, isn't it? Okay, let us just move on, then. I was telling your father about my life experiences."

"Great! Mom-stories. I definitely have to hear this."

Life began to change for me my senior year of high school. I was always involved with diverse groups of people, and that exposed me to different places—different ways of doing things. David, the last guy that I had chosen to date was the popular guy who all the cheerleaders wanted, so of course I was disliked by an entirely new group of girls, but that didn't bother me so much. The way I saw it, David wanted me, and he was super cute.

I had not had sex with him or any other boy for that matter; I had decided after Rodney that it wouldn't be easy for anyone to get to me in that way. Looking back at it all, my behavior might have been childish, but I enjoyed the power that I held over them. And after all, isn't that one of the powers women have?

They soon discovered that I made the rules, and the rules could change at any time. I learned that from my old friend Kelly. The rules were subject to how I felt or the attention I received. For the life of me, I do not know why any of these boys continued to want to go out with me. I only showed interest or made time for them when it was convenient for me.

Kelly had begun attending Spellman College in Atlanta. She would give me updates about college, and her stories were amazing. So, I jumped at the opportunity when she invited me to visit during my break. I asked my mom and she said yes, but only if I paid for my plane ticket with my own money. I think her request was only a test to see if I would do it. It was important to her to start teaching me some real-life values.

At the time I did not have a job, but I took it as a challenge. I got a job at Burger King. It was easy because one of my childhood friends already worked there. This was my first time ever working in fast food, and although I knew that this was not for me, I had a plan which I held on to very tightly. I worked there for about five weeks, putting burgers on the grill. They would not allow me to do anything else, but I was fine with that because I was only there to save up the $250.00 I needed for my plane tickets, and maybe a little extra for spending money of my own. I knew Mom would give me some cash to spend, but this would surprise her. And it felt good to have actually earned it.

"Kennedy, I really didn't think you would stick it out!"

"What do you mean, Mom? I knew you were only testing me."

"You're right. It was a test. I wanted to see how badly you wanted to go, and I wanted to know if you could accomplish something you felt was difficult." My mom looked me in the eyes.

"Well, I really do want to go, and I think it will be a great learning experience."

"Don't give me that 'learning experience' line. I'm aware that this is strictly about you and Kelly having a good time."

Once I purchased my plane ticket, I stopped working there. The friend that helped me get hired was disappointed that I quit after such a short time. She had a goal of becoming a manager there, which was fine by me. I wished her the best but… I was off to ATL.

It was homecoming week at Spellman. Kelly had me all excited about the parties we were going to attend. This was going to be the best trip ever, and it changed my perspective of my young life so much that I started looking forward to going to college.

Kelly had planned a perfect trip. I was exposed to the magnificent pageants they had on campus. The girls were so beautiful and intelligent, but I was blown away by their talent. It was unlike anything I had ever seen. Every night, all week, there was a vast array of parties to choose from. One night it would be a party with house music, another night it would be go-go music, and another would be jazz. My favorites, though, were the Florida bass music parties. Even though Atlanta wasn't far away from Florida, Spellman had a lot of students from across the country, which meant Florida bass music was foreign to most of them, But once they heard it, they loved it.

If you were from Florida, you received a tremendous amount of attention, and everyone just assumed you knew the dances that went with the songs. I think the music gave students that were not from the South the green light to let the inner bad boy and hoochie mama show. Also, during my visit, Spike Lee was on the campus shooting his movie *School Daze*. We were privileged to act as extras for the movie. I was loving it. Somewhere out there is footage of me dancing in a Spike Lee movie!

The life here was not one I was used to or had experienced before. Living in the dorms, eating in the cafeteria, and meeting groups of college girls was all very new to me. Most of these girls came from upper-class families. They were very nice, though some were snooty. But that did not matter to me because I felt like I belonged. Everywhere I went, I was made to feel welcome.

Kelly's cousin was a musician for the musical, *Mama I Want to Sing*, so he got us backstage passes for that as well as the Doug E. Fresh concert. College was so different from the small town I was raised in, and I remember wishing at the time that I didn't have to return.

Spellman was a life-changing experience. After that visit, I just knew I had to go to college. The experience gave me a certain resolve to improve. I knew that I had to make some major changes in order to get accepted into a good college, so when I returned home, I began to scrap a lot of the activities I was involved in and focused on the things I needed to do, like taking the required classes. And even though I was late preparing for college, I was determined.

My grades were only average, so that was a concern. But I knew that with the help of God, it could and would be done in time to get accepted. I felt like a fish out of water during this process. None of my high school friends were talking about going to college. It seemed so strange to most of them. Also, a lot of my friends from school were younger than I was, so I was alone in what I was doing. My mom didn't know anything about the process either, but she did her best to find me the resources I needed to make the transition, and with the help of my school guidance counselors, it was starting to look as though it was really doable, like it was really going to happen.

I finally convinced one of the girls from the neighborhood to get on board with going to college so I could at least have someone to prepare with. My mom hired tutors and bought SAT and ACT study materials to improve my scores before the final submission dates. I became reserved and focused. I knew that life was about to become serious and I could not bear the thought of failing. I wanted out of the small town. I wanted no part of what it was offering. I made sure I did not fail.

My mother was so proud to announce to the church that I had been accepted at Bethune Cookman College - BCU. I knew she was proud of me, but I must say I was a little shocked when she stood before the church with my acceptance letter making the announcement. The congregation cheered and congratulated me, but all I could think of was that there would be no more playing the piano for the church. It was the one thing that I had never missed a day of. No matter how late I stayed out on a Saturday, I was faithful to it. It was what I had been doing every Sunday since the age of fourteen.

"So, Mom, can I expect to have all the same fun you had while visiting Spellman?" Kylie's lips curled up into a sneaky smile.

"Uh, young lady, even though they are entertaining, your mother is telling you her life's experiences for you to learn from them. Not necessarily to emulate them. There are some things you may be able to do and others that you won't as long as I'm still alive." Greyson was the consummate daddy.

"Oh goodness, Dad! You just don't want me to have any fun, do you?" Kylie grinned at him in an attempt to play up her Daddy's little girl persona, the one that almost always got her what she wanted from him.

Greyson pursed his lips and puffed up his chest, mocking the 'me Tarzan' stance. "That's exactly right. You get me, kiddo!" Greyson held his composure for a minute until Kylie and I started laughing. Then he burst out into fits of laughter that lasted until he was out of breath.

It is not always easy for a woman to share some of the not-so-nice sides of herself and her past with her husband. It can be difficult to tell your truth and show your imperfections to anyone. However, it was different with Greyson. I shared everything with him. Even the ugliest, darkest corners of my life. I knew Greyson would never judge me.

I had not planned on sharing with Kylie, too, but as a mother to a teenaged daughter, there are some missteps I took in life that I did not want her to repeat. So, her coming home earlier than expected and me sharing with both of them was certainly divinely orchestrated.

"Sweetheart, you will get to do plenty of fun things when you go off to college. And you'll make your own mistakes no matter how well your father and I try to prepare you. We just always want you to be respectful of yourself first and others second. We want you to understand that every situation comes with boundaries and mistakes often have unpleasant consequences. That doesn't mean every mistake will be a bad one. Sometimes they can lead to unexpected surprises that open new doors for us in a good way. We've raised you to use your mind so you can think clearly for yourself." I was open with Kylie.

"I am opening up to you now so you know that in life we all make mistakes, and sometimes, in spite of those mistakes, we can still end up on top. I somehow managed to be nominated for Woman of the Year, that's nothing but God's anointing over my life and a lot of hard work, and I know He has placed the same anointing over you and your life. I want you to always remember that Kylie." I hugged my daughter tight, the way my mom used to hug me. I still missed my mom's hugs.

SCHOOL DAZE

I ALWAYS FELT LIKE I had to be tough or hard when it came to having Phillip as my biological father. I wanted to hide who he was—the role he played in my life. As a child I acted out with behaviors because I didn't know how else to express myself; as a teen, I discovered that it was always easier than facing my problems head-on. I often did things for no reason, things that made no sense and were destructive. However, in my mother's eyes, I could never do wrong, so she never disciplined me. This lack of discipline made me a spoiled brat, and everyone knew it.

I had busted my butt to improve my GPA and SAT scores to create a college application that would gain some recognition. My mother was proud of me because she never really knew how I was going to turn out. She may have had her doubts, but she never expressed them, at least not to me. And I doubt very much that she would have expressed them to anyone else. Despite everything, though, her prayers and preparation had gotten me through it all.

Just like the young peacock that wandered into our backyard this morning, I was always barreling through life chasing anything that grabbed my attention, as mindless as a bird pecking for worms. But thank God there was always someone there to guide me.

I loved being in college, and Bethune Cookman was perfect. It was close to home, which was great for me. If I ever got homesick or wanted to see my mom, it was only two hours away. I was still a needy spoiled brat who did not know how to wash my clothes or handle the other responsibilities of day-to-day living that other young adults my age had learned.

Besides that, my mom was getting older. She was almost seventy, and I was not ready to move too far away. So, knowing I only had a two-hour drive if I needed to get home quickly gave me great comfort.

Having a car on campus my first year of college turned out to be a big mistake. I soon became known as the girl who drove the Fiero. I was at every single party, both on and off campus. I was constantly on the go doing something. My friends and I never had a dull moment. We traveled to the away games and every other thing that caught our fancy. I really loved the freedom that college offered, but I also knew I needed to concentrate on my grades, or I'd soon be out.

I became close with Gi-Gi, a freshman girl who also had a car on campus. Gi-Gi was from Atlanta. She came to BCC with a legacy; her brother had graduated from the school two years prior. Between the designer clothes and the overbearing personality that kept her involved in everyone's business, there was a part of her that was lovable.

If we were the only two going somewhere, we would use my car, and if it was a large group, then we would use her car because it was larger. It was a way for us to save gas and it gave us the opportunity to bond and expand our friendship.

Once, I used her car to drive to Tallahassee. It was Florida A&M University's homecoming and one of my friends from Jack and Jill was pledging a fraternity. It was Alvin's second year at FAMU, and he was on the Alpha's line. His family had a long history of pledging Alpha. His grandfather, father and both of his brothers were Alphas. Everyone from Jack and Jill was thrilled for him. Once the word got out that I was going to FAMU, I had a list of girls who wanted to join in. There was no problem choosing five beautiful girls from a lengthy list to travel to Tallahassee, especially for homecoming.

Alvin did not have a roommate and had arranged for us to stay at his apartment for the three days we would be there. The responsibilities of pledging would have him busy and away from home for the entire week, so his apartment was perfect for the six of us. Every chance we got, we cheered him on during pledge week. His line brothers were in awe that six beautiful girls from a rival school were cheering and encouraging him.

At the end of the week, it was time to return. We shared the drive home taking turns driving when someone got tired. However, thirty miles from the campus, we got into a minor accident on I-95. Thankfully, no one was injured.

Once again, I had been driving so I felt it was my responsibility to find a local mechanic to repair the minor damage to Gi-Gi's car. The mechanic assured me it would only take about a week to complete the repairs to the rear quarter panel and taillight. She was not too happy, but I assured her that her car would be okay, and I offered Gi-Gi my car until hers was repaired. A week later I paid for the repairs and returned the car to her. A few weeks later, the car broke down again with a mysterious engine problem that could not be fixed.

She argued that the accident that took place when I had her car was the cause of the damage, but this new problem involved the engine.

I guess she was trying to get me to pay for the damage, but it really didn't make sense. Here was a girl whose family obviously had some money, and she was trying to scam me into paying damages for something that I was clearly not responsible for. I told her so, and our now fragile relationship completely broke down to the point that she thought she should be able to take possession of my car and keep it.

After a day of arguing with her, she left my dorm with my keys without me knowing. When I noticed my keys were missing, I went downstairs to find my car missing. I had not told my mother that I had been to Tallahassee or that I had a classmate's car repaired, so I was in a real bind and out of my depth. Things escalated quickly, so I had to share the whole story with my mom because I realized that I needed help getting my car back.

The constant arguing back and forth with Gi-Gi and contacting my mother had me emotionally drained. I was crying in my dorm one evening when my roommate came in. The same roommate who was never around when I needed her but somehow always seemed to show up at the wrong time.

She was furious at how I was handling the situation. My roommate was from Liberty City, and she did not take crap from anyone. I had met plenty of girls who were rough around the edges before, but none compared to her. She was "hood" and I do not mean that in a bad way. Let's just say when you met her you immediately knew not to cross her, so I wasn't surprised by her response.

"You pretty bitches kill me," she screamed. "Stop that damn crying and squash this shit. Beat that bitch ass, or they are going to run all over you on this campus. Look, Kennedy, you seem to think everyone likes you! Don't nobody like you 'round here. You need to stop going out of your way for people. You are too damn bougie if you ask me! Everyone sees that you are different, with the clothes and personality. But let me tell you, people don't know how to take you. And if you really want to know the truth, your ass is annoying. It's just too damn much!" She paused to take a breath and paced. She seemed to soften a bit. "This crying gotta stop. Call the police and tell them she stole your car!"

As harsh as her words were, they were what I needed to hear. In part, she was right…all but the fighting part. Crying was not going to solve this. However, I knew fighting in college—or anywhere for that matter--was the last thing I needed and something I could never tell my mother. I already felt bad about the way things had played out and making her come to Daytona to help get my car back.

I really enjoyed Gi-Gi's friendship. But now she hated me to the point she wanted revenge. She and her boyfriend hired someone to demolish the inside of my car. Her original plan was to only steal my car, but after I got it back from her, my mom had the ignition and keys changed. When they could not get into the car again, they broke the window, ripped the seats, and stripped the gearbox. The insurance company paid for all the repairs, so I was not too upset over the damage. I was happy knowing I had a car, and she didn't. The bigger problem was that she was becoming a threat and I was a little afraid of what she might do next.

Before the semester was over things escalated so much that we had a physical fight. Gi-Gi just would not let it go. Every day she continued to make threats toward me. She would go out of her way to show up wherever I was to harass me. Finally, I had had enough. She had to take a beat down.

It was a normal Saturday when Gi- Gi approached me on the yard. For weeks I had intentionally avoided her. However, on this afternoon the yard was packed with students and locals enjoying the spring day. I ignored her threats for well over thirty minutes but Gi-Gi wanted the attention, and I was more than ready to oblige her. She was very sure that she would come out the victor, unscathed by the 'pretty' girl, and she wanted as many witnesses as she could get. But she had a rude awakening when I landed several punches to her gut. I'd learned firsthand from Rodney how that felt, and I wanted to inflict that pain on her, to temporarily debilitate her and show some dominance.

She threw the first punch and I dodged it. I was not fueled by anger the way she was. I knew that emotions could skew our judgement, so I tried to keep calm. I focused on her eyes. This is the first rule of boxing. The eyes always give away your opponent's next move. Gi-Gi didn't have a next move, she just charged forward without any control. And having run track, my footwork was on cue. That and the fact that I was a dancer gave me a huge advantage over Gi-Gi. After a few more Rodney-like gut punches, she lie in the grass curled up trying to catch her breath. I didn't realize it beforehand, but when everything started to sync, I knew she didn't stand a chance.

Afterward, the administration organized a meeting with our parents to resolve the issues.

During the meeting, her parents and the school found out that her grades had dropped so low she'd lost her scholarship. Her father was furious with her.

He screamed at her during the meeting, in front of me and my mom. And anyone passing in the hall would have heard the tongue-lashing he gave her.

"There is no way in hell I'm paying for college when you had scholarships. I am so angry and disappointed right now!"

Gi-Gi looked totally humiliated and dejected. When it was all said and done, he withdrew her from school.

I, on the other hand, escaped probation and was permitted to remain in school. It was suggested that I press charges against her for damaging my car, but I just wanted it to be over. Seeing how defeated she was in that meeting, my heart sort of went out to her. It was obvious that she was a troubled girl, and I wasn't comfortable adding to her and her family's misery. What had been done was done. I wanted to put it behind me.

I think that was the first time I realized it was better to be kind than right. I felt good about that decision, and from that moment forward, I had a new attitude toward the plight of others, what motivated them to do what they did. Once again, I thought about Phillip.

14K

"KENNEDY, YOUR MOM SENT you to this school to find a husband." Those were the words a professor had the audacity to say to me my freshman year. It was a bold, presumptuous, and rude statement based on the fact that I could not answer one question she'd asked me. But her sarcasm was like a gut punch. And saying it in front of the entire class sure as hell did not help my self-esteem. But I was sort of used to sarcasm and doubt. In fact, I was learning to use it as armor. She didn't know a thing about me, yet she'd formed an opinion, and as I sat there looking at her, I knew I had to prove her wrong. I had become skilled at overcoming the odds and finding the victory.

It seemed that even a school of higher education, the one place you were supposed struggle, succeed, make mistakes, fall, get up, and be challenged, was just like any other institution or cultural group – filled with arrogant, self-righteous and bigoted people. She was basically saying, "Don't try little girl. This is not for you. Just find someone to save you." I never told my mother what that professor said to me, probably because it didn't matter all that much. My life was going to be bigger than what she was offering.

Given the car fiasco and this teacher's perception of me, not to mention that I really couldn't answer the questions asked of me in class that day, I made the decision to be less active socially in my sophomore year. I wanted to focus on studying and getting better grades so I wouldn't be embarrassed again in class. However, I quickly got bored and needed something to keep me busy, but I did not want to start partying and hanging out again.

At the advice of my biology professor, I decided to try out for the band's dance team. It was something I loved doing, and it would demand a lot of my time. That meant I would always have an excuse to say no when asked to go out socially, if I needed one. I later learned that my mother had arranged for the professor to mentor me and assist me if difficult times arose again. She had arranged for someone to make sure I did not chase every visible lizard or shiny object that was dangled in front of me.

I had never done this type of dancing before. Every dance lesson, performance, or dance school I had attended taught me theatrical dance. Everything was very technical, and nothing reflected cultural ethnicity. I was generally the only black girl, and if by chance there was another black girl in the group, for some reason I was the one picked to be out front receiving the attention. The older I got, the more I disliked being front and center. It wasn't the reason I wanted to be part of dance and baton twirling. Being the token or the only one or the first one seemed to turn people against me. The black kids and parents in my small town thought I was trying to be white, and the white parents thought I was too black, which meant they didn't want me involved, especially if I outperformed someone's daughter and was selected over her. By the time I reached high school, all the blacks were cheering me on. I guess they figured, "This heifer isn't going to quit, so let's get behind her." I had become so technical and precise with my performances that white fans were cheering as well.

But becoming a 14 Karat Gold dancer, or 14K as we were known, was something altogether different. It was nothing like any dance lesson I had ever taken or any show I had ever performed in. The moves were almost erotic, and if you know anything about historically black colleges and universities, it's all about the band and the dancers. No one went to the football games just for the football at any HBCU.

The halftime show was the thing. Almost everyone stayed in their seat during halftime. It was like moving around during communion at a Baptist church. You better not do it.

You just did not want to miss the performance or as they said, "the show." You could bet the band was going to give chest-high steps, spins and moves to their version of the latest songs. The band at Florida A&M University was known as the Marching 100; however, it was the Bethune Cookman drum majors, with their leaps and backbends, touching the turf with their heads, that got everyone's attention.

Bethune Cookman's band sound was precise and accurate to detail. They could only be characterized as perfect conformity to sound and dance moves. As great as they sounded it was all about the 14K dancers. We got all the attention. We were the perfect collaboration of sights and sounds. The 14Ks performed jaw-dropping, choreographed, Broadway-chorus-line moves that were rhythmic and provocative.

But dancing was dancing to me. I was a natural at almost everything I trained or practiced for, and I was convinced that this would not be an exception. There could be up to sixteen spots for dancers. It all depended upon the talent level. There could be as few as ten spots if there was not enough suitable talent.

Every day we trained for four hours, sometimes in the hot Florida sun, but I loved it. And the more we trained, the better I got and the more I loved it. I even noticed my physical appearance changing. I had well-developed abs and a nice round butt. I was in better shape than when I was running track.

I saw it as a privilege to be chosen. We performed every weekend and people would line up for autographs and photos. It was like being a celebrity. The homecoming performance was always great; however, you were not officially a 14K until you performed at the Florida Classic.

No pressure. There were only more than fifty thousand people screaming and cheering for us when we took the field. And we had their undivided attention. I had performed in performing arts centers, parades, convention centers, and at Disney, but none of it compared to or prepared me for the Classic in Orlando. People would begin to line up just to watch us enter the stadium. They would line up to watch us enter the field and exit the field. The ground moved and the stadium rumbled like a small earthquake during our introduction. My mind was completely blown away by the cheers that thundered through the crowd during our performance. It was two minutes of pure ecstasy that no words could describe

The word had made it to my hometown that I was a 14K dancer, and to my surprise I was greeted by what seemed to be every person from my town when we exited the field. I could not believe it as they screamed my name. I was the only dancer on the squad to live close to Orlando. All the other girls were from other states or cities much further away, which meant there was a lot of support for me that day. It was amazing, and I was in heaven. At every turn, someone screamed my name. Some of the faces I recognized, but most of the time, I did not have a clue who was screaming for me. I had been in performances where people cheered because of the show. I had even been in performances where people cheered simply because I was the only black performer, but never because it was me, Kennedy.

From that day forward, my life had forever changed! Things were never the same for me on campus or at home. The school had unwritten expectations and rewards for us. None of us ever stopped being 14Ks, whether we were performing or not. We were always expected to be on the clock, with hair and makeup done at all times if we were in public. The school used us to our full potential. We were the school's ambassadors. And we had to maintain a certain GPA, so all in all, it was grueling, time consuming, and one of the best experiences of my life. It was work being a 14K, for sure, but every one of us loved it. We would not have given it up for anything in the world.

When I did visit home, I was treated like a celebrity. I found it intriguing that all the whispers and reminders of my past seemed to have vanished, replaced with people stopping by my house to have photos taken. The same older women who used to make comments under their breath about my father, my adoption, and what they considered my snobbery now asked if I needed anything for college.

As for the men, well, all they simply wanted was to say they knew a 14K. I would catch them staring at me, and every so often one would get the courage to say something to me or ask me out. In my mind, I was the same skinny kid who none of them gave a thought about, and they were the same country boys who were trying to sleep with every girl in the neighborhood.

Dancing as a 14K gave me some of the best memories of college. In fact, I would say my sophomore year was my best year at Bethune Cookman.

BROKEN HALLELUJAH

What are our expectations? What should they be? Are the things we desire within reach? Do we even know what our reach—our potential—is? I sometimes wonder if what I had expected of my life back then was what really got me to where I am today, or if I just got lucky being in the right place at the right time. Was it divine intervention that brought Kim to Phillip and then to Mary?

Surely there must be some truth to this, otherwise why do we strive for anything in this life? And if we have a clear idea of the path we want to take, when is it right to do so? If not now, then when?

As a young woman in college, I also wondered how long it would take for me to get what I wanted out of life. Would I know it when I got it? Would it be handed to me or would I be searching for a long time to find it. And when I did get there, would there be some left for me?

I was thrilled to begin my sophomore year with my best friend, Jillian, the youngest of three sisters from Nashville. Jillian and I had become roommates toward the end of our freshman year.

It was odd how our friendship began. There was one guy in particular who was trying really hard to pick her up, and she looked like she wanted nothing to do with him. I happened to be standing nearby, so I pretended to know her just to be a distraction to him. That was how we bonded the first day we met!

In her squeaky voice, she said, "Girl, these Florida boys don't give up."

"They are persistent."

We laughed together, and from that moment on, we were as thick as thieves.

As our friendship grew during freshman and sophomore years, I realized Jillian always attracted the wrong guys and often fell in love with them—or at least that's the way she described it. Whenever she was in the grip of some obsession over a guy, we did not spend much time together, but when we did, we made the most of it.

"No, thank you. We didn't order that," Jillian said calmly.

The waitress looked toward the bar and whispered, "It's from the two gentlemen at the bar," and placed the two margaritas at the table. Prepared to hand over two fake IDs, Jillian and I said thank you and gave a nod toward the bar. But the waitress never asked for them, so we returned to our conversation, ignoring the drinks that had just arrived and the men who'd sent them. Jillian was intrigued by the admirers.

"I've never had anyone send me a drink before like this, have you?"

"Yes, I can say that I have, a few times in fact. I'm surprised you never have.

While we were laughing, the two men approached the table making every attempt to look good.

"I'm John and this is Chase. May we join you?"

I looked briefly at Jillian, who had lowered her eyes trying not to look at them. She was a bit naïve.

"Please." I motioned to the two empty seats at the table. But I had no intention of spending the next couple of hours conversing with our new guests. It was obvious John and Chase had predetermined who they had interest in, so we went along with it for a while. It was clear John had his eyes set on Jillian the moment they sat at the table. Chase was a tall, light-skinned guy with light green eyes, and quite good-looking, so I was completely okay with their choices. As it turned out, he was polite as well as handsome. We fumbled through our conversation, trying to find some common ground, and once we did, all our nervousness melted away.

Chase was a spoiled only-child like I was. He said he could relate to how I felt about not always fit in. Being an only child presented challenges, so we had that in common. He simply chose to deal with it differently than I did. We began dating, and after a couple of dates and a few months, Chase officially became my boyfriend. It was not until then that I shared with him that I was a 14K dancer. At first, he was a little bitter toward me. Maybe he was jealous. Or maybe, because I hadn't revealed all my information from the beginning, he felt I'd lied to him. Maybe he knew that 14K dancers received a lot of attention and he felt threatened in some way, thinking I might be playing on the side. But he soon forgave me because he knew that he had chosen wisely.

I had a rule of not telling guys I was a 14K right away. There is something about those two words that tested a college male ego. For some reason, it caused them to lose their mind. Most guys viewed dating a 14K as something to conquer, or at best, as his showpiece. I decided early on when I became a 14K that I would not be someone's trophy. I was aware of how guys talked to the other girls in the group and how their self-doubt and insecurities often became the biggest issue during their dating. It simply did not make any sense to me to be involved with someone with those issues. If they got to know me first, I reasoned, they would take the news better.

Our relationship had grown so much that over the summer break we visited his mother, Dr. Morgan, in Arkansas. Dr. Morgan had worked hard to create a career that was nothing short of astonishing. I was blown away by her success. She was Vice President of Academic Affairs—part of the president's executive cabinet--at Philander Smith College, and a commissioner on the local school board. She also chaired the board of the local television station and hosted a TV show interviewing prominent people of Arkansas. I was intrigued at how one woman could do so much; her day started early and ended late, yet Dr. Morgan was a sweet, down-to-earth, intelligent countrywoman who cared about people. She always saw and looked for the best in everyone. She was a role model for me—an example of the type of career woman I could admire.

Once we returned to college, Chase moved off campus while I continued to be busy with the band activities. We spent as much time together as possible even though we both carried challenging schedules. Things were perfect with Chase and me. However, I started to lose my interest in college. I had a strong desire to return home to spend more time with my mother even though I despised the small town I grew up in. I did not say anything to my peers, but Chase knew that I was not returning for the spring semester, so he decided not to go back to school either.

I tried everything I could think of to persuade Chase to stay at Cookman. But he was adamant in his decision. As he put it, he did not want to be there if I was not there. I did not have an explanation to give my mother or anyone else who inquired or pushed, but I refused to return. There was this strong gut feeling that I did not understand at the time, yet I knew I had to follow it.

Returning home, I got a job with a victim advocate program as a secretary, something I knew nothing about. After working there for three months, my mother became sick with cold-like symptoms. After a few weeks of being sick, my mom's good friend, who was a nurse, became more concerned. She convinced my mother to have some tests done. Chest x-rays did not reveal a cold but something much worse--breast cancer.

I was not sure about what was going on or how to handle all the sudden responsibilities that I was now expected, and wanted, to take on. I had no medical knowledge to fall back on. Hell, I cannot even remember a time my mother was ever sick, except for a cold. Yet here we were facing a battle with cancer.

I often wonder what prompted me to make the decision to leave school that semester, but I'm glad I did. The nagging intuition that I needed and wanted to go home to see my mom is something I'll always remember. And to this day, I always follow my gut feelings. I think if more people stayed in touch with their intuition—that little voice that nags us, the one we so often ignore—the world might be in a better place. Instead, most people just go through life by rote, keeping to their daily routines, living by the clock, stuck in jobs they hate, and never taking chances or leaving room to live out their dreams.

I was very thankful for the job I had because my employers and coworkers stepped in and helped me with everything I was facing. Chase was also there through it all. But I just wasn't prepared for this immense responsibility.

The next week, my mom was scheduled for a mastectomy. My mother never appeared worried, scared, or distracted during any of this. She simply wanted to continue running her businesses and fulfilling her assignments at the church.

My mother had organized for her staff to help with her recovery once she was released from the hospital. Once she was well enough, she had a friend of hers contact an attorney to complete a will for her. She arranged for all the houses to be deeded to me. I was to become the owner of both businesses, and whether I wanted to run them or sell them was up to me. They would be mine to do with what I wished. But I wanted none of it. I just wanted my mother to return to health and everything to go back to being the same as it had been. She was the only one who I felt absolutely loved me, and no one and nothing could replace that or her.

I sat motionless at my desk staring out at the parking lot. I could hear the phone ringing. People went about their business. Life moved around me, but I was empty of all thought. I had been tense and anxious all morning, but the phone call of my mother's admittance to the hospital had left me numb.

I felt completely alone as I made my way to the hospital. When the elevator door opened, I was afraid of what awaited me. I entered her room, sat next to the bed, and held my mom's hand as we waited for the doctor to return. *What is it about hospitals and beige walls*, I wondered? Nothing was said, and no tears were shed as we waited. It was as if we knew our fate, but in those few moments, I felt love as pure as heaven itself.

When the doctor returned to speak with us, we both had fallen asleep. He patiently waited for us to awake before delivering the news that my mom's cancer had spread throughout her body.

"I'm sorry, but there's nothing we can do. The cancer is inoperable. We will use the standard protocol of chemo and radiation, but I suggest you get all your affairs in order," he said to Mom. "We'll keep you as comfortable as possible during your ordeal."

The only thing I could think to do after receiving the news was to call Dr. Morgan. I placed the call in the middle of the day, but I knew her busy schedule usually never allowed her to be home during this time of the day. I was not sure if she would answer her phone. To my surprise, she answered. I cried as I told her that I was at the hospital with my mother, the walls were beige, and the doctor had just told me my mom was dying.

She patiently allowed me to gather myself, and calmly said that if anything happened to my mom, she would take care of me like a daughter, and I could live with her until I finished college.

My mom lay in her bed half asleep, still singing "Hallelujah" when I returned. Without thought, I curled up next to her and began to sing along. Afterward, she took my face in her hands and turned it toward hers. The smile her face wore spoke of a profound inner peace.

"I know what the secret chord is, Kennedy!"

I smiled. I could see the peace that God had placed on her.

"I think you have some news for me, Kennedy." I shared with her the conversation Dr. Morgan had with me. I no longer felt afraid once I lay my head in her lap. A few moments passed before my mom spoke.

"That will be the best thing for you to do, my dear."

This was the last real conversation I had with her. The following day was Mother's Day. I arrived at the hospital with flowers and orange slices. I placed them on the table and crawled in the bed with her. She died a couple of hours later with me lying in her arms.

I soon began to understand that gut feeling I had about leaving school. God had moved me in the right direction. He had placed me in the correct spot for what was about to occur. I knew I was placed on my job for this reason. They aided and comforted me through the process, and they also encouraged me to go back to college. Losing my mother devastated me. How could I go back to school? How would I be able to concentrate on my studies, or my dancing? It seemed in some way to be sacrilegious to try to be happy, to be pursuing dreams when she was gone. When I would never see her again.

But it was comforting to have Chase with me. For the next two months, I would have to manage a household, the businesses, and my life without my mother, and then make my transition to Arkansas to live with Dr. Morgan and Chase.

GROWING PAINS

TWO MONTHS LATER, I was in Little Rock, Arkansas, with Dr. Morgan and Chase. They welcomed me with compassion, and I felt as though they did everything they could to make me feel at home with them, but it took me a while to adjust to the unfamiliar surroundings. My new circumstances inhibited my ability to focus on school and at times it all seemed a little too much to handle.

I lived in constant grief of my mother's untimely death. She was irreplaceable, and no matter how much Chase and his mother loved me, it simply did not fill the emptiness that I was feeling.

The idea of living in this world without her scared me. Her love for me was the one thing that kept me moving forward, but now my grief over losing her was keeping me from doing just that. I knew she would not have wanted me to remain the way I was, filled with misery that was palpable.

Would I be able to fulfill what I needed to do to become all that I was destined to become? All the things Mary had wanted for me, hoped and dreamed for me? Everything she did was with my future and welfare in mind. It was time to shake my misery and move on. I didn't want to. I didn't want to forget her. I wanted her to always be with me, but I needed to find the line where debilitating grief met realism—the life I must get on with.

Dr. Morgan honored her word. She allowed me to live with her and she began to care for me as if I were her very own child. She overlooked all my unattractive faults. I was still spoiled and accustomed to having someone do everything for me. I didn't cook or clean, and I wouldn't know where to begin doing laundry. Simple things like sorting and washing, folding and putting my clothes away. It was disgraceful. I am not sure if Chase's mom felt sorry for me or if she was just allowing me to grieve. I am so embarrassed about it all now, because I didn't contribute anything to the household. I don't think I even picked up a dirty plate from the table after I'd finished eating. Thinking about it, my behavior was awful. She had allowed me to continue that routine, but in my heart, I knew the time had come for me to grow up and be responsible.

The following year, both Chase and I enrolled at Philander Smith College. At school, there were a few sympathetic people, including Chase, but a lot of the kids stayed clear of me. No one wanted to be around someone who is a downer, and although my grief was legitimate, it was still taking over everything I did. Slowly, I met and made friends at this new college. During all my grief, I met some great people, and we all shared the same goal - graduating.

Their friendships distracted me from the loneliness and slowly my mood began to improve. My new friends were motivating.

Chase always started school on a positive note. However, after a month or two, he would stop going. I never said anything to Dr. Morgan about him not attending his classes because of her position at the college. It wasn't my place to say anything, and she probably would have known without my help.

I also learned to use Dr. Morgan's influence to my advantage. For instance, I knew when to mention that I was from Florida, that I was an only child, both of my parents were deceased, and I was living with Dr. Morgan. On most occasions, it gave me favor with my professors. Everyone knew Dr. Morgan and wanted to be in her good graces. I used this often.

Even though college seemed to be getting a little easier, my emotions were coming undone again. Maybe I'd jumped back into a full school schedule too soon. All I knew was that I really needed a break from everything outside of the classroom so I could put all my focus on school.

Truthfully, there was not much to say or discuss. I had already mentally checked out on everything and everyone--Chase, Dr. Morgan, going to church-- anyone or anything close to me. School was the only thing that held my attention and held me together.

My friend, Lauren, and I had been in the club for an hour. All responsibilities were fading away, becoming nonexistent in my mind as I drank my second margarita. Lauren and I had hung out from time to time with some of our mutual acquaintances, but this was our first time partying together. We had met during a study group on campus. We had always discussed going out partying but never found the time. Lauren's boyfriend demanded a lot of her time in the evenings, but this weekend, he had traveled to visit his parents, so it was the perfect opportunity for us to hang. And I wanted desperately to escape it all.

For some reason, no one was asking us to dance. I've heard it said that men can be intimidated by pretty girls. They assume that they have so many other men vying for their attention that it would be a waste of time, that they wouldn't stand a chance. So they don't bother. And the pretty girls remain lonely due to a misconception.

"Screw this," I shouted. I grabbed Lauren by the hand and we hit the dancefloor, with me slinging my hair wildly. I could feel the music coursing throughout my body, the heavy base that came through the speakers pounding and moving me like a dervish. I was giving the club just enough of those Florida 14K moves, and I did not care who was watching or what they thought.

I was dancing so hard I had not noticed that Lauren had stepped off the dance floor, nor did I notice the tall, dark handsome guy dancing behind me. When I turned around, he just smiled and continued to dance with me as if we knew each other. I was in my zone, and I didn't mind him one bit because he was fine as hell. He had the sexiest pair of brown eyes.

Next up was a slow song, and before I could exit the dance floor, Mr. Handsome took my hand.

"Please stay! May I have this dance?"

I shook my head no, but my body never moved. He put his muscular arms around my waist and pulled me close to his chest.

"I noticed you and your friend the moment you walked through the door."

"I seriously doubt that."

He flashed an enormous smile. "What's your name?"

"Nice smile." It was a quick response; the only defense I could think of.

He chuckled. "Don't try to redirect the question. What's your name?" Only this time when he asked, he removed his hands from my waist and took both of my hands and held them, staring directly into my eyes.

This fine dude had persuaded me to look into those brown eyes. And that's when I lost my advantage. Things started to become a little fuzzy, maybe from the margaritas, maybe form the music or lights. All I knew at that moment was that we were the only two people on the dancefloor, alone among the dozens of other dancers, like there was a mist hanging around us and no one could see us. Hell, at that point, we could have been the only two people in that club and I would not have known the difference.

"Kennedy." My own voice sounded distant and foreign to me.

"It's my pleasure to meet you. You are absolutely gorgeous, Kennedy."

Smiling, I replied, "I'm glad you think so. I guess I'm alright."

"Girl, I have been a lot of places, seen half of the world; let me tell you, you are way beyond alright. So, do not ever sell yourself short. Just trust me on this one."

"Okay, so maybe I'm being a little modest." I must have sounded like a schoolgirl when I spoke. "Thank you."

I had never dated a dark-skinned guy or thought of being attracted to one, but Mr. Handsome had my attention. He was different, quite different. We danced a few more songs then stepped outside to talk. It was the first time since my mother's death that I did not feel empty or alone. He told me he was visiting Little Rock and had to return to Jacksonville, FL. I thought to myself, *why would you visit Little Rock, especially if you lived in Jacksonville?* Mr. Handsome explained that he was in the U.S. Navy and had to be back on base in four days. It was unfortunate, he said, that we had just met.

Lauren had been looking for me. She opened the door and saw us together, in a lip lock that was far too premature for this relationship. She screamed, "Kennedy, what are you doing? Stop that!"

I pulled myself away from Mr. Handsome's kiss. I do not know when it began, and I do not know how it would have ended if Lauren had not shown up.

"That was incredible," Mr. Handsome whispered. "I never have evenings like this."

"Neither do I," I said. I pulled a compact and my lipstick from my clutch and reapplied it. And all the while I could sense him watching me.

"Let's go, Kennedy."

Mr. Handsome and I exchanged numbers before Lauren dragged me away toward the parking lot. We hopped into the car and drove off.

When I got home, Chase met me at the door. At some point, Lauren had called her boyfriend and told him about the entire evening, and he had called Chase. I did not want to deal with the problem even though I knew I was wrong. I had gotten caught making out with someone new and wanted to see where it would lead. I was out of control, but I did not care about anything or anybody. I was hurting inside and wanted everyone to hurt, too, even the people who loved me. It seems I was back in form, arrogant, selfish and independent of rules and responsibilities to myself or anyone else.

"Damn, Kennedy. How could you?"

"I'm sorry." Even though part of me did not care.

"Sorry? Is that all that you have to say right now?"

"What do you want me to say, Chase?" I screamed and began to walk away. It was a classic defense mechanism. Make the other person feel guilty to divert attention away from your own mistake.

Ask another question in response to a question. Clearly that did not make things better.

Chase got directly in my face. He was close enough for me to smell the vodka he had guzzled while waiting for me to get home.

"I allowed you to come and live here with me and my mother and she agreed to it. And this is what I get in return? You think this is appropriate? It's bullshit, Kennedy!"

I pushed him away to create some distance between us. I wasn't afraid. I was more disappointed in how my great evening was unfolding. It was late and I needed to sit down.

"You don't own me Chase, and you didn't *allow* me to do anything."

Chase interrupted me before I could continue. "I thought we had an understanding, Kennedy. I thought we were an item. I know that you miss your mom and it's clearly taking you a long time to adjust, and for that I am sorry. I understand you need a change, but when you make that change at least make sure I'm alright with it. I want you out. Get out!"

I got up from the chair and started pacing the floor. My head began to pound from the arguing. Even though it had been only a few minutes, it seemed like we had been at it for hours. I pointed my finger at him in anger.

"You have no idea. This is the hardest thing I have ever had to do. You have a mom. Everything you need is right here for you. I have no one. I'm all alone in this world. Besides, Dr. Morgan promised. She promised my dying mother, Chase, so I'm not going no f-ing where!"

Chase and I argued until daylight. I had pushed him to his breaking point. Maybe it was my way of breaking ties. Hurt him so much that he'd want to leave me, and I would be off the hook, so to speak. It wouldn't be my fault.

He needed an escape from my madness. Being cordial and understanding was no longer working. He really wanted me to get myself together or get out.

"I will need an answer by tomorrow morning. Go get some sleep and decide what it's going to be, Kennedy." He left the room, slamming the door behind him.

No sooner did that door slam then I had the phone in my hand. I called Mr. Handsome to wish him well. I told him that I was having problems with my boyfriend. I told him that I was an only child, both my parents were deceased, and I was homesick. I told him that I didn't know if he was just being nice or what. Then he suggested that I come to Florida with him. Out of nowhere, I said yes without thinking it through.

I told him I would go only if I could drive my car. If nothing else, it made me feel like I had some control over what was rapidly unfolding. Mr. Handsome changed his arrangements to accommodate my demands. It felt like I was running away, and it felt good, so I just went with it. I packed my things, went to his sister's house where he was staying and picked him up. I was on my way to Florida with a man I'd met only a few hours ago, without saying goodbye to Chase or thanking his mother. No explanation. Just moving on in my typical way, with no consideration for anyone but myself.

Along the ride, we got to know each other a little. It felt good being with someone new, and although my actions felt crazy, I was grieving and just needed something adventurous, something that would make everything seem okay.

Mr. Handsome was exceptionally smooth. He was very skilled with his words. He told me how he would treat me and all that he would do for me if I was his girlfriend. It all sounded nice, but I knew something about smooth-talking men. Somewhere within the fantasy he was spinning was the truth. I don't know if I trusted him or not, but I was still willing to go along.

We had to go through Mississippi en route to Florida, so I told him that I had relatives living in Mississippi and would like to stop and see them. They were my siblings from my biological mother, Kim. But I did not tell him that. I did not need him knowing too much about me just yet.

I had not seen them in years. Even though their father, Edward, had brought them to visit me every other summer when we were kids, our visits became few and far between once I got older and went off to college.

As much as I loved being an only child, I liked the idea of having siblings. Edward was a very nice man; every time he brought them, he seemed to be more worn and tired than the last time. My mother always asked him to stay awhile so he could rest, but he would leave the kids and go back to Mississippi. I think those few weeks every other summer were his opportunity to regroup and energize himself from being a single father–a widower under the constant pressure and responsibility of raising children on his own.

When we arrived, they were so excited to see me. We caught up and made small talk. They did not ask too many questions about Mr. Handsome, and I was not giving up too much information. Heck, I did not have much to give anyway. I had asked him to stay in the car while I caught up with them. He was cool with it and did not give me any problems about not meeting my family. My siblings offered for us to stay with them, but it was way too early in the relationship. I didn't know much about this guy and was not comfortable with the area they lived in, so we decided to get a hotel. Checking into the hotel, I began to feel like I was with a stranger. And I was. What was I doing here? I must have been out of my mind to agree to this. If I wanted to go to Florida, I could have gone on my own.

I told him I was feeling uncomfortable being in a hotel room alone with him. He assured me that he would be a gentleman and that nothing would happen that I did not want to happen. I went along but I waited until he got into the shower before opening his wallet and taking his military ID.

The next morning, we continued traveling to Florida, and for some reason, once we were there, I felt better just being back. The first thing we did was go to the base. He showed me around and explained his job to me during the tour of the ship. He also introduced me to some of his friends and told them he was going to be looking for an apartment. He was a day early returning to base, so we checked into a hotel for the evening and immediately began planning our search for an apartment. We mapped out which complexes we would visit the next day because our time was short.

The next day, I awoke in a panic. I guess I was finally coming to my senses. Something was telling me, "Kennedy, you have to go back to school. You have already paid thousands of dollars for your classes." At this point, I desperately needed an exit strategy. I just could not live the kind of life he was proposing.

Once we found the apartment we wanted and it was time to write the check, I had to put a stop to it all. I told him that I had to go back to school. Mr. Handsome looked at me, smiled and started laughing. I did not understand why he was laughing. He asked the apartment manager to excuse us for a moment and we stepped outside.

"Kennedy, I have been waiting for you to tell me that since Little Rock. What took you so long?"

I looked at him, a bit dumbfounded.

"I could sense that you had gone through something. I wasn't sure if you are running from something or to something. But you need to remember that life gets easier, so take your time and live it."

"Thank you so much. Someday, I may tell you all about it."

"Fair enough, but I'm still getting the apartment. I need a place to live. If you ever want to get away, you are more than welcome to come here.

Before he signed the lease, I handed him his ID and said, "I think you might need this." He just rolled his eyeballs and grinned at me.

We finished at the apartment and drove back to the hotel. He packed my bags into the car. "Ms. Kennedy, it has been my pleasure." He kissed me and I was on my way back to Arkansas.

Once I returned, I went back to Dr. Morgan's house like nothing ever happened. Both Chase and his mother were overjoyed to have me back and to know that I was fine. I told them that I had driven to Florida to see my relatives. I'm sure they didn't believe me, but they never asked another question, and it was never spoken of again.

"OMG, Mom! Were you a female version of a player?"

"Not at all, sweetheart. A least I do not think so. I was always clear about what I wanted and made that known to every boyfriend—everyone I dated. They knew my intentions, and I always reserved my right to change my mind. Especially when it came to a boyfriend or relationship that clearly had no future."

"Mom, that sounds so harsh."

"Think about it, Kylie. How many relationships are made to last at the age of 17 or through college? So, here I am dating a boy, my mother had passed, and I had just moved to the area. Everything was out of order. What are the chances that would have become a forever relationship?"

"Mom, more importantly I want to thank you for sharing how you dealt with things after your mother died. That could not have been easy. I don't know what I would do if I lost you, Mom. I can't even think about it." A small tear formed in Kylie's eye.

"Looking back at all of it, I think I temporarily lost my mind. My mother was my world, and even though Dr. Morgan and Chase tried desperately to create a new life for me, I was emotionally unhinged. I was in a place where I didn't care about anything or anyone; a part of me wanted to keep the people that cared about me at arm's length, and another part of me was simply bored and in need of excitement." Greyson held my hand.

"Yeah, I was a complete mess. I would go from happy to sad in a heartbeat. I was totally lost without my mom. She literally did everything for me."

"Like you do for me?" Kylie's revelation stopped me in my tracks.

"What? Kylie, what are you talking about?" I stared at her confused.

"Seriously, Mom! You have never disciplined me; only Dad has. I have no idea how to cook, all I do is straighten up my room, but I never have to do any other chores. I come home and my clothes are freshly washed and folded and lying on my bed. I get up in the morning and there's breakfast ready and waiting. I've never washed a dish or cleared a table or vacuumed or dusted. I've never picked up my shoes after kicking them off at the front door, yet there they always are, neatly lined up in my closet. School and activities are the only things you make me adhere to. You guys just got me a car. Should I go on so you can see that you treat me like your mother treated you? I mean, I'm not complaining, mind you. Thinking about it now, hearing your story, I'm very grateful. I never actually thought about it before, but I realize now that responsibility has to be part of life. Without learning that, how can we go on to be responsible for anything else that matters, like children or a career?"

Greyson gave me a look that required me to reflect on Kylie's statements. I was more like my mother in how I raised Kylie than I realized.

"Wow, honey! I never thought of it that way, but you are absolutely right. I do treat you how my mother treated me. I guess I wanted to shelter you like she sheltered me." The revelation of that statement shifted the room for me.

I was like my mother. But more importantly, I had opened the door to my dating past with my daughter. I was not ashamed of my beliefs or how I had chosen to live my life, but it was becoming clear to me that perhaps Kylie didn't share those beliefs.

They say we should always strive to make the lives of our children better than our own. That we should give them advantages that will help them succeed in life, not just with money or a career, but with values and integrity.

I vowed at that moment to require Kylie to begin doing some of the household chores, if only temporarily, so she could better understand what was involved. Even if she became wildly wealthy and could afford servants, it would serve her to know what they would be going through, the work they would be doing on her behalf.

I had no complaints about Kylie. She was a good kid, but this would help her understand that not everyone had a life like she had, and it would make her a more tolerant person in the long run.

Taking a deep breath, I prepared myself for the barrage of questions that were certain to come from my inquisitive sixteen-year-old. My interrogation was averted by a phone call before it could start, and with that, my dating past was forgotten.

"President Kylie Davenport speaking!" Placing her hand over the phone she whispered, "Mom, I have to take this call. Do you mind?"

Greyson and I both looked at each other and smiled. In unison we spoke, "Absolutely, Madame President."

No sooner did the words fall from our then lips she was bolting from the room.

"That was close," I said, turning my attention back to my husband.

"Babe, what's up with Mr. Handsome? Did you really drive from Arkansas to Florida with a total stranger?" Greyson laughed trying to lighten the mood. "I could tell you weren't ready to explain yourself to her so let's move on before she returns."

"That sounds good because I definitely don't want her to hear this next part."

YOU DON'T HAVE MY PERMISSION

I HAD NEVER CONSIDERED LITTLE Rock home, even though Dr. Morgan really went out of her way to make it feel that way for me. Everywhere we went, she would introduce me as her daughter, and I was beginning to enjoy it. Through Dr. Morgan and my circle of friends, my contacts expanded; my grades were better than they had ever been. Neither Chase nor I were home a lot, so we managed to avoid each other for the most part. When we did meet, it was generally just in passing, and there was little more than a frosty polite acknowledgment of the other's presence.

I liked Chase. He had integrity, was smart and well-mannered, and I sort of missed being close to him. Eventually things got better between us as we remembered why we had been attracted to each other in the first place.

The following semester, I pledged Alpha Kappa Alpha Sorority, Inc. Chase had pledged a fraternity while at Bethune Cookman, and he began spending more time with his fraternity brothers at Philander. During the first two years of our relationship, we flourished, but now things were changing between us. Chase had started to drink every day, and when he wasn't drinking, he was smoking weed. He also started to lie about everything, including things that did not require a lie. I began to question why I was even with him—who he had become. I guess I still felt a sense of obligation to his mother, who had taken me in out of the goodness of her heart, but I needed another outlet, someone or something to take my mind off Chase and his mess.

That's when Murphy Honeycutt came into my life, and she was just the distraction I needed.

Murphy Honeycutt was tall and caramel-skinned, half-Dominican-half Nigerian. She was the girl all the guys noticed first. Maybe it was her height. Maybe it was her body. Or perhaps it was her piercing eyes.

When she walked on the campus, you could feel the guys staring. You also could hear the women whispering to their men, "Don't you look at her," which, since men will be men, they could not help but do anyway.

Despite all of her physical beauty, it was her personality that was most attractive. She had a way of making you feel like you were the only person who mattered when you talked to her. Most people found themselves opening their soul to her.

Chase is the one who introduced me to her, and we hit it off immediately. He also warned me to stay away from Murphy. He was never a jealous boyfriend, but he feared I would receive too much residual attention when I was with her. Chase always enjoyed the attention I brought to him in his hometown, so he knew this was a real possibility, not just a jealous pipedream. He would perk up when people would say I was the cute girl from Florida with an over-the-top fashion sense and a convertible. But he was not pleased when he found out Murphy and I had become close. Murphy was outgoing like me. She sought adventure and played by her own rules...just like me.

Over the summer, we spent time doing whatever we could think of, but mostly shopping, especially if we were having a difficult day. Chase and I were already starting to drift apart, but it was his anger about me spending time with Murphy that had contributed to our final breakup. The time had come. I finally decided it was time for me to move out and live on my own. For the first time in my life, I would have no one to fall back on, even though Dr. Morgan had promised to continue to care for me. I was grateful to have had Dr. Morgan, but I was determined not to need her.

I had never lived alone, and I must admit I was afraid. I found a furnished two-bedroom apartment at a reasonable price, and because I did not like the idea of living by myself, Murphy became my roommate. Jamie and Lori were my two line sisters. We had pledged our sorority together and, including Murphy, I had built some solid friendships. We did everything together. It was like having a family again.

I tried desperately to forget my past, and that past—along with certain people associated with it--soon became a distant memory. That did not include my mom, of course. She was the best part of my past and would forever be with me. But now I was beginning to see that I needed to remember the good times with her and stop mourning her death. It's not what she would have wanted for me.

I told my friends that I was an only child with deceased parents. If they asked too many questions, I would deflect and redirect the conversation. This was my defense. It was my way of controlling how much information I was willing to give about myself, and it kept me from having to talk about the painful issues of my past. In other words, everyone was on a need-to-know basis.

Murphy returned home excited and animated after the Keith Sweat, Bell Biv DeVoe concert she had gone to. She rushed in and immediately began to share how she met the band and how she was invited to the show in Nashville, Tennessee, which was about four hours away. She asked me if I was interested in going. I didn't have classes on Friday and only had plans of reading ahead over the weekend, so it was an easy decision.

"Of course," I quickly responded.

We hurriedly packed and hit the road in her Corvette. We had taken a few road trips together during our newly formed friendship, mostly to University of Arkansas in Pine Bluff, and we always had fun. I didn't see any reason why this trip would by any different in that sense, so I had no reason to say no.

When we arrived in Nashville, we only had about two hours before the concert started, so we quickly got a room and dumped our stuff, showered and changed, then went to the venue.

The concert was mind-blowing! Murphy mentioned her connection and we were escorted backstage, where there were other fans, industry people, musicians, and a table filled with food and drink. As we watched from off stage, I remember thinking that Murphy had landed a great connect.

One of the managers was tripping hard over Murphy that evening, so after the show, we went to breakfast with him at his invitation. Murphy played along enough to see where things were headed, and by the end of breakfast, he was like putty in her hands. He told us their next stop was Atlanta. He also suggested that we join them. Murphy told him that we were college students and would need to think it over. Before we thought too long, he reached into his pocket and pulled out a handful of money.

"Look, ladies, it would mean so much to me if you would join us in Atlanta," he said as he counted out a few hundred in crisp new bills—six hundred dollars in total. He also promised to book a hotel room for us. Murphy and I excused ourselves to discuss the offer. We returned and told him we would accept.

It was funny to me how things were unfolding. My best friend, Lynn, who was also my godsister, attended college in Atlanta. I phoned ahead and told her I was coming to town with Keith Sweat and Bell Biv DeVoe. She was in disbelief with the idea of me traveling with a band and wanted proof, so we made plans to meet up when we arrived so that she could see for herself.

I had never been a groupie, and I wanted to make it clear to Murphy that I was not going to start now. If this wasn't on the up and up, with no funny business expected of us, I was out.

Once we arrived in Atlanta, we checked into our room, picked up Lynn, and spent the rest of our day with her. We stopped by the venue just as they were doing a sound check, and we were able to spend time with Murphy's guy. We wrapped up with Lynn in time to make it back to the room to prepare for the show.

Atlanta is a great city to party in, so after the show we hit the clubs and partied all night.

The next morning, there was a knock on the door. It was Murphy's guy. She answered the door and they sat in the lounge area of the room. I could hear him talking as I lay in bed. It sounded like he wasn't happy about not getting to spend time with Murphy. He and Murphy talked for a few minutes to resolve any misunderstandings before he went to the bathroom. Returning from the bathroom he passed my bed and deliberately grabbed the covers and yanked them from over me.

"Kennedy, it's time to go," he said, and he walked out and slammed the door.

"What are we doing?" I asked Murphy. "And what's wrong with him?"

"It's your lucky day. We are going to Orlando!" she said, waving another five hundred fifty dollars in crisp new bills in the air.

I sprung up from the bed. "Girl, that man is going to want something." Then, I jumped out of bed and ran to the shower. "Breakfast is on you, Murphy," I screamed.

She smiled and replied quietly to no one, "No, breakfast is on him."

We drove to Orlando for the concert. We were very content with the way things were working out. Even though we had been traveling with the band, we never saw them off the stage, which was fine for Murphy and me. Murphy's guy eventually got his date with her, so he was more than pleased.

Although we knew we needed to stop what we were doing and return to school, we would be fortunate to have only missed a couple of days of classes if we returned to Arkansas. But we were really enjoying this road trip, so we decided not to return to school yet and continued the tour with the band.

Miami was the next stop, and we could not miss the chance to go to Miami. There was always so much happening there! Money flowed through this city the way iguanas flowed through the canals of Florida. It seemed like everybody had it and they were willing to spend it.

It was the last stop on the tour, and we had had a ball the whole way. Murphy's guy checked us into our room, but this time, he said we would have to share a suite with him and his roommate. We didn't think much of it because by that point we had spent so much time with them that we had begun to feel comfortable. Besides, he had reserved a two-bedroom suite, which meant Murphy and I would have a bedroom for ourselves.

The roommate was an older guy in his thirties. The entire trip he had been polite even when I told him that we were not there to participate in what some of the other girls that were around were doing. We weren't groupies.

After the Miami show, we went to dinner with the entire band and their manager. The champagne flowed and everyone had a wonderful time. Murphy and I had been going all day, and by the end of a late dinner, we were done. There was no more partying in us. We drove to the hotel anticipating a long lie-in. I wanted to sleep til noon. I was out like a light soon after I crawled into bed at 3 am.

My dreams were troubled. I dreamed of the boys back in my small town, ganging up on me, chasing me, trying to get me down on the ground. In my dream, Chase stepped in with a sinister grin and started to part my legs while the other guys laughed and pointed their fingers at me. I woke with a shock.

At first, I thought I was still dreaming. All the champagne that I'd consumed left me feeling groggy and lethargic, but not enough to know that there really was a guy in my bed attempting to spread my legs. The roommate.

I sprung up, kicking and screaming.

"What are you doing? You filthy pig! Get out of here! Get out!"

He rolled over on the bed bleeding from his nose. My frantic kicking had landed squarely.

"What the hell, man. You kicked the shit out of me, bitch."

"You better be happy that's all I did. I did not give you permission to touch me. Where's Murphy? How did you get in here?"

I was enraged. I grabbed the clock from the nightstand and began swinging it like a lariat. I clocked him in the side of the head and dared him to take a step closer.

"C'mon, asshole, you wanna play, let's play." I was so infuriated I didn't realize I was still naked.

"I will beat the shit out of you right here, right now you bastard!"

He ducked and dodged the flying clock, looking for any place to escape being hit again. I hit the mirror and it fell from the wall. The small TV came crashing to the floor as he tried to take cover behind it.

"Why are you running, big boy? And where the hell is Murphy, you contemptible mother…? You're disgusting. Do you realize how old I am? Do you know how old *you* are? Oh, my god, you sicken me!"

I swung the clock and smacked him in his back. Then again in the head. Murphy and her guy had been in the next room and rushed in. The clock casing had shattered leaving only the inner components attached to the cord, but I continued swinging. Without a word, Murphy began kicking the crap out of him.

"Why are we beating his ass?" she managed to say among the fray.

I growled, "I woke up to this piece of trash trying to touch me without my permission in a place that *definitely* needed permission! I was asleep and woke up to find him in my bed! I did not ask you to touch me!" I screamed. "What were you thinking?" I stared him down and he tried feebly to answer. "That wasn't a question, jackass!"

Murphy gave him a final kick as he lay curled up on the floor before rushing over to me and wrapping me in a sheet. "It's ok, Kennedy. I got you. I got you."

Murphy's guy walked over to his battered friend and punched him in the face. Blood trickled from his mouth. All he could do was roll over and moan.

"I am not going to jail for your dumb ass. Get your stupid ass up."

The two men left the room, the one dragging the other by his shirt collar. Murphy sat me on the bed and tried to comfort me. I was shaking with adrenaline as every muscle in my body convulsed. A lump of emotion had built in my throat, and now that I wasn't screaming, I was finding it difficult to get words out. But the last thing I wanted to do was let anyone see me cry.

I looked around the room at the destruction I had done and managed a weak smile. The room was trashed. It was then that I noticed his wallet on the floor. I walked over and fished through it. I removed the contents and handed Murphy his driver's license. Turning on the broken TV. It made a screeching sound and tried to cycle through the channels before going completely black. The guys returned from the adjacent room. Without saying a word, he gathered his wallet while holding his bags. His friend shoved him out the door before he could say any other words. Murphy's friend turned toward us and apologized.

"Kennedy, are you ok? I'm sorry, and I will take care of the damages." He turned and walked out the door.

I jumped to my feet and quickly snatched the driver's license from Murphy's hand. I opened the door and screamed holding the ID in the air so they both could see it.

"Hey, asshole! Phillip is going to kick your ass."

Once I closed the door, Murphy just stared at me, and after a long pause, she sat again on the bed.

"Kennedy, who the hell is Phillip?"

I was so engrossed in the story, reliving every sickening moment of it, that I didn't realize I had blurted out Phillip's name. I wished I could shove the words back into my mouth, but I couldn't.

Thank god Kylie had left the room because I would have hated for her to find out about Phillip that way.

Greyson and I looked at each other. Thank God for my husband who always knew how to save the day.

"Honey, I can't believe you threw that out there. You used the Phillip line?" He laughed it off. "You'll sic Phillip on anybody you can't stand."

"Hahaha, very funny," Humor has a way of healing. Yet, a part of me felt bad. It was the first time any uncontrolled thoughts or words regarding Phillip had escaped my mouth.

A BIG ASS WAD OF MONEY

WE LEFT ARKANSAS WITH a total of seventy-one dollars, a full tank of gas and the intention of getting on the road and returning home after the Nashville show. We'd witnessed one of the greatest R&B shows of all time and had traveled four states and nearly thirteen hundred miles. Every moment had been spectacular. Well, maybe not every moment.

Murphy and I sat at a little Cuban cafe on Bayside. We had somehow managed to spend all the cash Murphy's guy had given her, and we were now down to our last sixty dollars. The cafecito was strong, but it gave us the jolt of energy that was needed while we planned our return to Little Rock.

We were sitting in the sun enjoying our quesitos, freshly removed from the oven. We could feel life being restored with every bite of the warm cheese pastry and robust coffee. Steam swirled from my cup, and for a short while nothing mattered. After all, we were in Miami. There was no need to hurry.

Thirty minutes into our euphoria, I focused myself. "Murphy, I have a plan."

"I'll take anything right now seeing how my mother just turned us down."

"And you find that hard to believe, Murphy?"

Prior to arriving at the café, Murphy had called her mother in an attempt to get money. Her mother could not believe that we had traveled to Miami. She was even more upset we were not in school. I think her exact words were, "If you girls were smart enough to travel that far you better be smart enough to get back." Murphy rolled her eyes the whole time as she recounted her mother's words. She couldn't tell her mother that some guy we'd met on the road had given her eleven-hundred dollars and we'd managed to spend most of it.

I just laughed uncontrollably. "I'm sorry Murphy, but that's funny as hell."

"Well, I don't find it particularly funny."

"Ok, my bad. Listen, I've thought long and hard about what we need to do, and it's the only solution to make sense of our problem."

"I'm so glad you've given this so much thought, Kennedy. What do we do? Where do we go from here?" Murphy was spastic with her hands flying everywhere. "All I know is, my mother better put money in my bank account! I think she will, but let's hear it. What is your plan?"

But Murph's mother's words were true. I was smart; we both were. It was time to step up to the plate and prove I could be on my own, think on my own.

"We simply have to make it to Orlando. On our way back, we will stop in Orlando where I can get money from one of my mother's businesses. I'm certain we can stay with one of my godsisters until Monday."

"That's a great idea but I was hoping we could somehow stay in Miami. You know, this is my first time here. I want to see what all the hype is about, Kennedy."

"Murphy, we have a half tank of gas, so it should only take a few more dollars to get us a full tank. We should have more than enough to see Miami and get us to Orlando. We'll still have about forty dollars to enjoy the city."

We continued enjoying the cafecito and watching the beautiful people passing by the cafe. Everyone that passed was beautiful. Just when you thought you had seen the last beautiful person, another group would pass. It was more like being on another planet. We sure as hell were not in Little Rock anymore! By the time we downed our coffee, we had already heard four different languages - Spanish, Portuguese, Patois, and Creole. If you were born and raised in Florida, you have an ear for these languages. It all was like music to us. The Ozarks of Arkansas did not offer different dialects. The closest thing being remotely different from English was what I referred to as backwoods mountain mumbling.

As we sat there discussing the events at the hotel and how it all unfolded, we laughed at the butt whooping we delivered to that jackass.

"A clock, Kennedy? What in the hell made you grab the clock?"

"Girl, it was the first thing I saw. I wanted to throw it at him but realized that it was plugged in. Turned out better than if I'd planned it that way. Man, swinging that thing felt good!"

"You were swinging it like you were possessed. Did you see the fear in his eyes? That brother looked like he wanted to be anywhere but in that room with you. And why were you naked?"

Giving her a stern look, I replied, "I was sleeping. And why weren't you in the room with me? You and I were supposed to share that bedroom since we were sharing that suite with them." I rolled my eyes at her. "Besides, when I get hot during the night, I take my bottoms off. That's why most of the time I sleep naked."

"Do you sleep naked at home?"

'Yes. Somehow I even manage to take off clothes in the winter."

It was at that moment I realized that ever since middle school I had begun to undress during the night because I would get hot. I never gave it much thought, and I am sure Chase didn't mind it at all. But it left me pondering the outcome on this occasion.

"If I'd had any idea either of those guys was coming into our bedroom, I surely would have had on something."

"I'm so sorry about what happened, Kennedy. When they came in, he wanted to continue to talk to me, and I did not want to wake you just to tell you I was leaving the room. When I stepped into his room to talk, that asshole was in the game room shooting pool and watching TV. New rule, if that situation should ever happen again, and I pray that it won't, we are sleeping in the same bed, and I will make sure you are properly dressed unless we discuss it."

"I have been sleeping naked this entire damn trip, Murphy! That little pervert tried to go down on me. I thought I was dreaming when he tried to open my legs. I better never see him again." I could feel the anger returning just thinking about it.

With a sigh, Murphy asked, "Are you okay? And who is Phillip?"

Just as Murphy asked about Phillip, two guys were walking into the café, which was good because I was once again about to think of a way to deflect the question. They stopped at our table and said we were the prettiest things they had seen that morning. Big whoop! False flattery got them nowhere, but thanks to them I had successfully managed to sidestep the question of Phillip.

After spending about an hour strolling around Bayside admiring the yachts, sights, sounds, and smells of the city, it had us craving more, and the afternoon sun was inviting us to the beach. South Beach was just around the corner, a fifteen-minute drive away. En route, we stopped to fill up the Vette. My mind wandered while I pumped the gas. Murphy slumped in the passenger seat to relax.

"Hey, you two!" Looking over from the pump, Roderick and Tim, the guys we'd met earlier at the cafe, were walking out of the gas station. "Man, Miami got some beautiful women. What a beautiful day."

His words caught me by surprise because I had not heard anyone say that since my father died. After some small talk, I told them that it was Murphy's first time visiting Miami and we were going to South Beach to tan and see the Versace mansion. They insisted on being our tour guides and taking us to lunch on South Beach. So, we agreed to it because frankly at this time, we were winging it and trying to decide if we were going to head back to Orlando and then Little Rock.

As Roderick and Tim showed us around the beach, they explained how it was divided into groups. Models, gays, locals, and tourists. They all had an unwritten section on South Beach. To the untrained eye it went unnoticed, but Miami had a lot of unnoticed things taking place right before our eyes.

After a quick class, we could spot the locals from the tourists, gays from straights, and models from everyone else. It was interesting how a lot of the models looked. They looked like most people but only thinner and taller. I was shocked to see that most were not as pretty as they appeared in print or on the runway.

After our lesson, the tourists began to quickly stand out. They all seemed to be overdressed for the city. Most wore matching outfits or clothing that they clearly had given a ton of thought to, while the locals seemed to have on get-up-and-go clothing, the kind you would wear at home on any day of the week. Except here in Miami, no matter what they wore, it was sure to be tiny and revealing.

We found a wonderful place on Ocean Drive for lunch. The guys told us what parts of the city to avoid and where to go for entertainment and food. The conversation was light and without any particular purpose. Murphy and I were pleasantly surprised but happy they weren't trying to hit on us or pick us up. During lunch, we shared with them that we had traveled, unplanned, to watch a concert - a concert that offered more fun and adventure than we could have imagined. We told them we were low on money and thinking of going to Orlando to stay with a relative. Before we could finish, Tim interrupted.

"I have a friend with a condo over on the beach. Would you girls like to stay there for a night? You're more than welcome."

Of course, we gladly agreed.

"Are you sure, Tim? We really wouldn't want to impose."

"You're kidding, right? Believe me. This is not a problem."

"Hmph. Whose place is it? And don't go thinking we're some kind of freaks because we're not. Don't make us call Phillip," Murphy sarcastically replied.

I looked at Murphy, shocked by her response. I had still not provided her any information about him. She must have read my mind and saw the confusion on my face. With a wink from her, I knew to just go along.

"He's my business partner, and I, for one, don't think y'all are freaks," Tim tried to assure us. "I know what freaks look like. He lives in Palm Beach and bought the place as an investment. He got tired of driving back to Palm Beach when he was here, partying in Miami."

"Like I said, we are not no freaks!" Murphy poked out her lips.

We all laughed.

He made a phone call, and we were on our way, following Tim and Roderick in their car to spend a beautiful night in a condo in Miami Beach. Free of charge. Once we arrived, we had the concierge escort us up to the room just to be safe. Tim assured us that everything was legit and there would be no funny business. They had no ulterior motives. Once we felt secure in our room, Tim and Roderick told us that they would return in the morning to take us to breakfast.

The following morning, Murphy and I sat on the balcony in disbelief at how things were going. We laughed thinking no one would ever believe any of it. What great luck!

At breakfast, Roderick and Tim continued their hospitality. Roderick explained that he was from Nashville. He said he had lost his mother and grandmother within the year and moved to Miami to be close to his best friend because he needed a break. Tim owned a business making gold teeth--mostly for rappers. The two men were completely different in every way, but they said they had formed a brotherhood at Tennessee State.

Back in the condo, I stared at the ocean from the balcony. We had come back up so Murphy and I could change our clothes. My mind drifted to Chase and what he was doing. I thought of calling him but scratched that idea rather quickly. I wondered why life could not be this peaceful always. What was preventing me from living in a high rise overlooking the ocean, not having a care in the world? How much work did it take to get there? I glanced up to find Tim standing at the doorway looking at me.

"You look like you were having a moment. I didn't mean to interrupt it."

"Um, I was. This view is absolutely beautiful."

"Yea, I know. I come here to get away from it all, to clear my mind and think about what I need to do next."

"Can I ask you something? What made you stop and speak to me and why are you being so sweet?"

"You mean you really don't know?" Tim looked shocked at the question.

Shrugging my shoulders. "Not a clue!"

He sat down and pointed toward me.

"You're necklace. It's what made me stop."

"My necklace. What does it have to do with anything?"

"It's not just the necklace. It's the charm that you wear. You're an AKA!"

"Skee Wee," I held up my pinky finger as I said our sorority call.

"When I was pledging at Tennessee State, if I did not learn anything else, I learned to take care of my sorority sisters. They constantly pounded that into us in the mornings, afternoons, and evenings. Take care of your sisters. It was preached almost as much as brotherhood."

"You mean to tell me you're my brother? You're an Alpha?"

"That's right. I'm an Alpha."

"Wow. This is crazy. I pledged earlier in the year."

"Basically, it's imperative to make sure you thrive while you're in my presence. The thought of just leaving you in a time of need simply wouldn't sit well with me, sis."

'Thank you so much. I'm—we're very grateful."

It should not have come as a surprise that he was an Alpha. His impeccable manners and behavior toward me showed me he was different. A guy who was not just after a date, a pickup, a party. Tim was my brother in Greekdom. He told me that he had an obligation to take care of me. People often say that historically black colleges and universities are special places. All I know is Tim's generosity was developed and learned at an HBCU.

I was blown away by his words and began to cry. I could not thank him enough that morning.

Before we left for Orlando, they filled up the Corvette, and checked the tire pressure and fluids. They even gave us travelling money. We never made it to the Versace mansion, but entering the on-ramp of I-95 north, Murphy and I had the biggest smiles you could imagine.

I think Murphy kept repeating, "I'm pledging all the way to Stuart, Florida."

The first thing I did when we arrived at my godsister's house was call Tim. As soon as he picked up the phone, I shouted, "Thank you, Tim. We made it safely." Murphy also screamed thank you in the background. I told him we intended to stay with my godsister before continuing on to Little Rock. We made plans to stay in touch and to visit him once he returned to Nashville.

Although our visit was unannounced, Sonya welcomed us. Sonya was a few years older than me and her sister, Lynn. Lynn and I became friends in 1986. We developed our friendship at church, and once my mother died, her parents became my godparents.

Sonya told us she had a guest coming over, a promoter from New Jersey. It was during the time of Def Comedy Jam, so promoters were going all over the country trying to cash in on the explosion of young comics. She offered us tickets to the show, but we declined. Murphy and I were exhausted from the drive. All we wanted was sleep. Besides, we did not want any more surprises. We had concluded that we had pressed our luck the entire trip. All we wanted to do was shower and go to bed.

We were awakened early the next morning to the sound of screaming and yelling coming from the kitchen. We lay in the bed motionless with the comforter pulled up to our noses listening to the argument.

I contemplated going to see what was going on, but I was too afraid, so I just lay there. We did not know what to think. The promoter seemed to be mad. He was screaming and cursing. Things were escalating to the point we thought that they were going to fight. We were scared.

Sonya hurriedly came into our room to tell us that he was angry because some of his money was missing. I looked at Murphy and threw my hands in the air.

"Sonya, why is he yelling at you?"

Putting her finger up to her lips, she whispered, "Shut the hell up. I have the money. This asshole wants me to undress to see if I have the money." Reaching between her huge breasts, Sonya pulled out a big ass wad of money. She handed the money over to me and whispered.

"This is what we are going to do. Get y'all asses dressed and meet me at Publix in thirty minutes. I will give you a cut and don't say a word when you leave this room."

Sonya turned and exited the room, returning to her yelling. I assumed she was thinking, "Let me get these chicks out of my house, then we can finish."

Murphy and I quickly dressed and got the hell out of there. Sonya was standing in the living room in nothing but her bra and panties.

"I told you I didn't have your money." I could hear her say as I closed the front door.

As soon as we stepped out of the house, we were relieved to be removed from the situation, but Sonya had placed us right in the middle of it. We immediately counted the money once we parked. Forty-eight hundred dollars! The thought instantly came to my mind, as I put all the facts together. No wonder that promoter was so angry. I knew that Sonya would never give us more than one hundred dollars being the cute little hustler from Jersey that she was. I also knew she hadn't counted the money.

I told Murphy that we should take twenty-five hundred out of it, give her the balance and tell her that was all she gave us. Sonya would never think that I would know how to beat her at her game. As a matter of fact, it was not the kind of thought I would have normally had. But it came to mind very quickly after I thought about all the times she had blackmailed and gotten over on me and Lynn.

When we met up with Sonya, I gave her the money and she raised her eyebrows in surprise; she obviously thought that there was more money than that.

"Sonya, that's all of it. That's all you gave us."

But she knew the wad she gave us was larger. She was mad as hell. She unfolded the cash and counted out two hundred dollars and gave it to us, then put the remaining cash in her purse. Slipping into her car, she looked at us and smirked.

"I know you pretty bitches got me." Then she sped off.

We got into the car giddy with excitement and started to scream. We had been so lucky! We could not believe all we had been through. It had been a crazy six days. We toured with a band, stayed in a condo on Miami Beach and then took twenty-seven hundred dollars home. It felt like we had won a lottery. With our sudden influx of cash there was no need to get the advance from one of my inherited businesses. The drive back to Arkansas had never been so nice.

Once we arrived in Little Rock, we decided to deposit the money into our respective bank accounts. The idea of having twenty-seven hundred dollars in cash at the house was not a good one. Murphy exited the bank in full laughter.

"What is so funny?"

"She put money in my account! My mother put two-hundred fifty dollars in my account the very same morning I told her we were in Miami."

"You mean to say we went through that thinking we didn't have money? I don't believe you."

Murphy held up a statement. "Here's the proof, oh ye of little faith!"

PARTY, PARTY, PARTY

My mother had the habit of praying for me. She had tremendous faith. It was a faith she had perfected every Sunday for hours on end in that little, hot sanctified church. The congregation only consisted of about fifteen people. They waved their fans and shook their tambourines waiting on the presence of the Lord. I remember sitting there as a child bored out my mind. I remember, in the middle of what seemed like chaos and noise, my mother smiling at me and whispering, "Kennedy, the Lord has ordained your life. He has great blessings for you." Even though I hated those long boring Sundays as a child, I now missed them and my mother.

But this is something I'd told Greyson long ago. He already knew that part of my history. My walk down memory lane was interrupted by the doorbell. The hair and makeup team had arrived, which meant it was four o'clock. They shuffled into the living room with all their equipment before I escorted them to my master bathroom.

Murphy and I had taken week off from school to stay "on tour" with the band. We had the craziest encounters along the way, most of them being lessons that could not be taught in a book. All of it was worth it for the experiences we shared.

After returning from our trip, Murphy and I rented a four-bedroom house. Our friend, Leonard, rented a room from us, and since my line sisters, Jamie and Lori, were always over visiting, they decided to just share the fourth bedroom.

Leonard was from Toronto. To this day, I have no clue how or why he was living in Little Rock; he did not go to any of the colleges and looking at him you just knew he wasn't from there. He spoke several languages and always talked about things none of us had a clue about.

We met Leonard at a trendy downtown restaurant one evening after a basketball game. He worked as a server. We had an enjoyable conversation with him while he waited on us and we gave him a bit of a good-natured hard time because we smelled weed on him. The three of us laughed so much that it must have taken thirty minutes just to take our order.

We even bought a puppy for our new home, a black Chow with a grey nose that we named Cornell. We gave him the name after Dr. Cornel West because we thought his big fluffy mane and grey nose reminded us of the political activist.

Our house was the best around. We always had parties that were loud and late, so I'm sure our neighbors hated us for that.

For months, we planned an over-the-top party for my twenty-second birthday. Leonard made an incredible breakfast for the four of us that morning. We loved having him as a roommate because he prepared meals for us every day (promising to give us his secret) and we never had to do laundry. These were life skills I never learned as a child—or yet as an adult--so this was great for me.

Our house was like a black version of Three's Company plus two. Besides, I'm sure he loved seeing four beautiful college girls: three of them constantly walking around in their bras and panties. Jamie was ultra-casual and lived in pajamas and sweatpants, but she had a conservative streak and could never bring herself to walk around in her underwear. We thought of Leonard as a brother. Besides, he was big into white girls at the time. Plus, he always paid his rent on time.

The guests all arrived with gifts and the right attitude to make the perfect party.

The thirty carefully selected guests were chosen because I knew they would not mind if the party were to get out of hand, which we had every intention of making happen.

The day was already off to the perfect start. Murphy's parents called in a favor and arranged to have the party catered by my favorite BBQ restaurant in Memphis. There was a DJ setup in the backyard and there was the surprise male dancer that I wasn't supposed to know about, but I had overheard Jamie and Lori conspiring together on the phone one evening securing him for the party.

Then there was the shocker that morning; a package without a return address; I was not expecting a package so I had no clue who it could be from. The brown paper wrapper had only my name, address and postage that gave me no indication where it was from. Inside was a flat white velvet box with the black Versace logo. Once I opened it, I immediately recognized the white tissue paper with the iconic gold Versace insignia.

The card inside the box read, "Happy birthday, sis! Hope this makes your birthday special. I am certain you and Murphy have something fantastic planned. From your boys, Tim and Rodrick."

I reverently rolled open the paper to find two pairs of black Versace leggings. Of course, Murphy and I were thrilled with our gifts. We may have never made it to the Versace mansion, but Versace still found a way to make it to us.

I did not have a boyfriend at the time, but I did not want to be completely single on my birthday, so I invited Enzo. Enzo had been trying hard to date me, but after a couple of dates, I did not think it would work. Enzo was your typical college guy. He was the type of guy I usually found myself attracted to. He was not a jock or the guy trying to be a player; he was simply a nice guy, but there was something about him that held me at bay.

Enzo was a tall version of Carlton. Yes, the "Carlton" from the '90s television show, The Fresh Prince of Bel-Air. The boy drank a glass of warm milk before bed every night.

By ten o'clock, all of us had a nice buzz going from the alcohol. Murphy and I were dancing when Leonard returned from his room.

"Who wants to drop acid?"

Staring at him, Jamie quickly spoke up. "Oh, hell no. I am out. You must be out your damn mind.'"

"Is it safe?" Murphy shouted.

Jamie yelled. "What drugs are safe?"

"Are the ones given to you by your doctor safe? Nothing has ever happened to me when I did these. I just tripped."

"Leonard, man, we are black people. We smoke weed. We don't do acid!" Lori's response was swift.

"Shut up, Lori! I'm not trying to pressure anyone, but you only live once. You're supposed to do dumb shit when you're in college."

We exchanged smiles and giggles in an attempt to hide our faces from God, ashamed of what we were about to do. One by one, we took our turn placing the small pieces of paper under our tongue. Murphy and I started to dance; the anticipation of what was about to happen filled the room. Lori and eight of the other guests who were partaking in this illegal activity did the same. It didn't taste like much, so we waited.

About an hour later, I was dancing on clouds. Murphy danced and held hands with me while we floated around the room. Everything was so beautiful, and I felt like I did not have any feet. Every emotion and sensation I had was enhanced, and my skin responded to the slightest touch. Murphy and I laughed and talked. We had complete conversations with each other, yet our mouths were not open or moving. I was trippin'.

"Heaven help me!"

She let me go, and I floated away into all the beautiful lights until I couldn't see her.

I do not know how long I tripped, but when some of my senses returned, I found myself sitting in Enzo's car kissing him. My body was engorged with sensation, and I was close to losing all control of it. We must have been going at it hard because I never heard Murphy shouting to get my attention. Enzo and I never saw her. Our kissing meshed our faces into one.

It wasn't until she climbed on top of the hood and began to jump up and down shouting "Kennedy, stop it, stop it, you don't even like him" that I noticed her.

I got out of the car giggling like a little schoolgirl, and within seconds I could feel my spirit float back into my body. That was my first- and only-time taking acid. I vowed I would never do that again.

Still hazy from the drug, Murphy helped me into the house leaving Enzo in the car. We fell onto the couch in uncontrollable laughter, our senses still heightened.

"Kennedy, I can't believe you!"

"What did I do, girl?"

"You were kissing Enzo."

"I was not. I don't believe you."

"You were Kennedy. You were kissing Enzo. You don't like Enzo."

"Did I really kiss him?"

"You were on top of him Kennedy!"

Our laughter was contagious; when I stopped laughing, Murphy would begin and vice versa. By this time, most of the guests had cleared out. It was late. Some had moved on to the club, but a few remained in the backyard smoking weed and swimming.

Sitting there on the couch, we assumed the house was empty, but through the music and the laughter outside, we could hear the faint sound of noises coming from the hallway. Like two intruders, we crept down the hall, trying to hold back our giggles. The acid still had us somewhat high.

As we got farther down the hall, we determined the sounds to be coming from my bedroom. Opening the door slowly we stood there in disbelief. I did not say a word nor did Murphy. We just stood there with our mouths hanging open, as if in a trance.

Leonard and another guy were having sex with Donna. And from where we stood, she was enjoying the attention. Donna was known on campus as the girl all the guys liked being around. However, none of the guys wanted her as a girlfriend. And now we knew why.

I was pissed that they had chosen my room, but I closed the door without saying a word and we returned to the couch. They emerged from the room a few moments later, their clothes partially on as if nothing had taken place. They all kissed as if Murphy and I were not sitting there.

Donna and the other guy made their way to the table and made themselves a drink while Leonard sat on the couch beside us and lit a joint.

"So, the three of you are going to act like nothing happened? Why were you in my room?"

"My room is dirty, real freaking dirty." Leonard spoke while exhaling a puff of smoke.

"Is that your excuse?"

"Yeah, my room is dirty; besides, you were trippin' outside with Carlton, I mean Enzo. I thought we would be done before you returned," he spoke with a sly half smile.

Taking another pull from the joint, Leonard walked over to Donna and blew the smoke into her nose before kissing her.

"Tomorrow I want a new comforter set, with sheets and pillowcases."

"Done." Patting his pockets Leonard stood up then walked to his room and returned, placing money in my hand.

Donna took another pull from the joint before asking, "You girls aren't going to tell anyone about this, are you?"

"Donna, I'm never the one to judge nor would I share what I just witnessed, but I'm pretty sure we won't have to. Word gets around, you know."

Before I could finish speaking, Murphy interrupted.

"Well, we won't mention you liking threesomes if you never say a word about us trippin' on acid, right Kennedy?"

"That's right! Not so much as a word."

With Murphy, Donna and I having come to an agreement, Leonard returned to his joint and took a long hit.

"Are you guys ready to keep this party going? When you're tripping you have to go to the club and dance it out." Leonard adjusted his clothes and stood to go. Murphy and I looked at each other and shrugged, then we followed him out the door.

A bunch of us piled into the car and began to pull off when we noticed Enzo asleep in his car.

"Wait, I'll be right back." Murphy ran back into the house, returned with a blanket and placed it over Enzo.

The Disco was a gay club, but they played better dance music than any other club around. We really just went there to dance and to stay up all night, but as soon as we arrived, one of the guys who came with us started freaking out because we did not tell him it was a gay club.

"This is a gay club," he screamed as the rest of us were paying to get in. He was causing a big scene. He became extremely upset and took off, walking away. But the rest of us stayed and partied until last call.

I do not know what time we got home, but the sun was up, and we found Enzo still asleep in the car. Still hungover, we managed to get Enzo from the car to the couch to finish sleeping off his high. I don't think I've ever felt as exhausted as I did after that party. I think we slept for the next two days.

The word had made its way around campus that we had had the best party of the year, but there was never a mention of acid. Everywhere we went kids asked about it and if they could be invited to the next one. People had really begun to exaggerate about what took place. There were rumors that there were strippers and a live band. But the best rumor I heard was that you could only enter the party if you agreed to give up all your clothes and party for three days, Friday to Sunday, without leaving. Whenever I heard that foolishness, I would only smile and say they missed a great party. And they would always end with "don't forget about me; I want an invite to the next one."

Thanksgiving break was approaching, and I knew that I did not want to travel back to Florida. I hated the holidays. Not having parents or a family that I really cared for made the holiday seasons difficult. Every year I never knew what I was going to do or where I would spend a holiday. I knew Murphy's parents were traveling to Europe over the holidays, but when Jamie and Lori told me they had decided not to travel home to Minneapolis, that made the decision to stay home easy. Since we'd all be together, we decided to cook Thanksgiving dinner. The only problem was no one had ever cooked a Thanksgiving meal. In fact, none of us had ever really planned a meal that involved anything more than a can opener, a drive-up window or paying a delivery guy.

For my entire time in Little Rock, I had either dined out or had my meals prepared by Dr. Morgan or Chase. Now, we had to trust Leonard to prepare everything. Don't get me wrong, Leonard could cook, but cooking a full Thanksgiving meal was a lot for any one person. And I knew now was not the time for me to try to learn how to cook.

Once Leonard got on board with the idea, the meal fell into place somewhat easily for him. We even got a few of our friends from California to join us for Thanksgiving. They did not want the expense of traveling back to California for either Thanksgiving or Christmas, so Cam and Riley were more than happy to join us.

Thanksgiving morning, we awoke to all the smells of a traditional Thanksgiving dinner. One by one we entered the kitchen where Leonard greeted each of us with a breakfast Mimosa, and we watched as he moved through the kitchen like he was in a choreographed dance. Every move was precise. Mixers turned, pots and pans clanged, and timers alarmed all to the aroma of sage, basil, onions, and other herbs I had not heard of. House music rang out from the living room and filled the entire house. The music and the savory aroma from the kitchen reminded me of childhood with my family. Leonard was proud and pleased to have an audience as he prepped and prepared the meal. He'd been at it for two days. The boy had skills. I could not help but be in a festive mood. Everything was perfect.

When we finally sat down for dinner, we were excited to see that he'd made turkey, oyster dressing, greens, mac and cheese, lasagna, and chocolate mousse cake. After dinner, we all sat around stuffed, drinking wine, and talking about what type of impact we would make in the world after college. We were like a real family, comfortable around each other and content with the world that day.

Lori wanted a career in politics, Murphy planned to be a sports analyst, Jamie was working toward a law career, and I still did not know what I wanted to do. I hadn't hit on anything that truly appealed to me yet. Even after all I had been through, even after having a professor tell me, "I think your mother sent you to college to find a husband." The nerve of that old heifer! Even after attending two colleges, I still didn't know what kind of career I wanted; what I did know was two things: I was not returning to the small town I grew up in and someday I would have everything that I wanted. It was just a matter of knowing what that was.

Jamie interrupted my thoughts.

"Kennedy you always tell us what you don't want, we know that already. Tell us what you *do* want." For the first time in my life, I stopped and thought. I knew she was right. I always said what I did not want. I began to cry as I sat there thinking. I have always been running away from my life, running away from my past, running away from my future, and running away from certain people.

I hesitated before pushing the tears away from my cheeks, the shaky words fell from my tongue. "I want to make a difference in people's lives. I want to leave their life better than they were when I found them. When people say my name, I want them to smile and know that there is comfort in it. I do not want to work, or should I say I don't want it to feel like I'm working."

"I want to travel the world and see all the things you see in magazines; you know, go places and do things that little black girls only dream of. I do want to be married someday. I want a husband who will allow me to be me; one who will cherish me and live to make me happy, who loves my over-the-top personality even when it's out of control and overly enthusiastic."

"I don't want comfortable. I want to be impassioned to have effortless mindless passion. I need someone who will kiss me like it is the only thing keeping him alive, and I want to be admired, touched, and smiled at. I want a man who misses me when I am not around. I want someone who is my equal in strength and commitment, who cares about the world, who has integrity, who is funny and smart and kind…" I looked at the faces of the others. I had their full attention. Then I smiled, realizing that I'd been going on and on about what I thought was the perfect man for me.

"Is that too much to ask?"

Riley began to laugh aloud, "Good luck! That fool ain't on this campus."

"Shut up, Riley!" I said good naturedly. "Oh, and I want to make a lot of money."

Jamie caressed my cheek and stared into my eyes. "Listen, Kennedy, over half of the people on campus don't know what type of career they want, so you're not alone in that area. Just keep working 'til you figure it out. Besides, your inheritance has provided for you during college. I know losing your parents sucks, but they have left you with a tremendous advantage in life."

Murphy sighed as something changed in her demeanor; you could also see the change on her face. "There have been countless times I start my day wondering *what the hell am I doing here*? Am I here just to appease my parents or am I here for myself? All the money my parents pay to this school and I am still not sure what I want to do. Sometimes I just want to see what is out there, but I can't tell my parents that."

"Yea, your parents would lose their minds."

After a few more emotional moments of crying, Lori, Murphy, and Jamie comforted me in a group hug. Eventually breaking the moment, Riley suggested we all take a road trip, a trip to California. And this trip…all I can say is wow!

HYPED FOR HOLLYWOOD

We started making plans for California right after dinner; everyone was on board and psyched about driving there during our Christmas break. A California Christmas had me so excited; I had always wanted to visit the west coast, so I was filled with anticipation. Murphy's parents had relocated there, plus Cam and Riley's parents lived there, so we had multiple options of where we would stay.

We only had eight to ten days. It would be a twenty-four hour drive straight out I-40, so we'd need to drive without stopping for the night in order to have more time once we got there. We'd take turns doing the driving.

Two days before our departure, our plan started to change shape a bit. Jamie and Lori decided to go home for the holidays. Their parents were not going to allow them to miss both Thanksgiving and Christmas. Riley's girlfriend was not going home for break so she would now be joining us, and Riley's frat brother, Malik, was going to go with us as well. Malik grew up playing basketball in California with Riley. For the sake of me, I can't imagine the transition from California to Little Rock, but Philander Smith recruiters had brought them there.

Murphy and I drove west followed by Cam, Riley, and his girlfriend in a second vehicle. Malik flew ahead to arrange some entertainment for us once we arrived. Malik's parents worked in the music industry; they both had worked on the TV show Soul Train and now worked for Sony Records. He promised to give us an unforgettable experience in California.

Halfway through our drive, we decided to stop in Las Vegas. We cut off I-40 and drove up Route 93. As we rounded a bend heading into the city, the lights of the Vegas strip appeared in the distance in a neon glow that filled the sky. My stomach tingled with excitement the closer we approached. It had been a long detour, but I knew it would be worth it.

The lights and energy of the strip were somewhat overwhelming. They pulled at every emotion I had; I had never seen anything like it. We were college kids with limited money, but that did not matter to us. We were determined to take advantage of the city and all that it offered.

It was everyone's first time in Vegas, and we didn't have any idea what awaited us when we pulled up to Caesars Palace valet parking. I could not believe that I was in Las Vegas! We were all tired from the twenty plus hour drive, but we were excited, too, so some of us went straight for the slot machines. But I needed a drink, so I circled the casino twice before finally taking a seat at the bar. I needed a moment to take it all in before I started to gamble.

I knew nothing about gambling. The idea of giving my money to a game where the odds were clearly against me made me cringe, but I did want the experience.

Waving over the bartender, I ordered a drink.

"What will the pretty lady have?"

"I would like a…wait, what would you suggest I have?"

"I have the perfect drink for you, but I'm going to need an ID."

"Sure!"

The bartender looked at the ID and whisked away. Just as she left, a gentleman sat beside me. His stare could be felt even through the smoke.

"My, my, you are beautiful; I'd really like to be your friend. Would you consider that?"

"I don't need a friend."

"I'm sorry; how can I be your friend if I don't know your name."

I crossed my legs and turned my back toward him, hoping he would get the not-so-subtle hint.

"Come on; don't be that way."

With my back to him, I sighed. "Sir, why would I come to Vegas and meet up with someone old enough to be my dad?"

"Hey, I'm just trying to be somebody's sugar daddy, that's all."

Just as I was about to really lay into him, the bartender returned with my drink. She could clearly see that I was agitated with the guy's unwanted advances.

"Joe, why are you bothering this young lady? Here's your drink, miss. That'll be twelve dollars please."

"Thank you." I grabbed my drink, left a ten and a five on the bar and slipped away to try my luck at the slot machines.

Returning her attention to the gentleman, the bartender said, "Joe, this is the third evening you've come in here trying to pick up women. I don't think it's working, and I say that politely."

"Why is that?" he said.

"Joe, you're drunk and way too aggressive."

"One of these evenings someone is going to say yes."

"Yeah, right!"

I got bored shortly after a few rounds at the one-armed bandit. A waitress had brought over two more drinks during my time at the money pit disguised as a game. These were on the house. I did not see the appeal in hoping three fruits would magically appear before me. Darting from the machine I wanted to explore the other areas of the casino and hotel. I figured everyone was enjoying themselves and would not want to end their fun just to have them wander around with me.

That third drink had begun to take its effect, and I now realized I was clearly separated from the group and lost. The casino floor was huge. I knew I would not be able to last much longer, so I found a nice older lady to help me find my friends. I told her that I had too much to drink and needed some help finding them. She was all too happy to help, and it was a good thing.

I passed out just as I heard someone shout, "There she is." I did not even get to thank the lady.

When I woke up, Murphy and the others were standing over me along with two paramedics and a casino manager. I sat up, a little woozy, but I seemed to be ok. My fainting, however, ended our stop in Vegas. I was full of fear because of what happened in the casino. I'd never passed out before and was concerned that there might be something wrong with me. What was in those drinks, I wondered.

The paramedics checked my blood sugar, and it was then that I remembered I had not eaten since breakfast. I had broken the cardinal rule when drinking. Never drink on an empty stomach! They gave me some orange juice and we were all pleased to see that I was making a quick recovery. No one wanted to make a hospital part of our trip. They suggested I get some food in me pronto, so we made a pit stop at one of the quick-snack stations on the casino floor and headed out to get the cars.

Four hours later we were in L.A. It indeed is one of the most beautiful cities I have seen. I was not prepared for this; it looked like the California of my dreams. It was gorgeous, it was Miami on steroids.

I had heard wonderful things about California, so I was filled with a great deal of joy when we arrived. We had planned to spend the first few nights at Riley's parent's house; he told us that his parents were conservatives with a lot of money. He said they had a large home in Englewood, but none of that really mattered to us. We were just happy to not have to pay for a hotel.

Riley's parents did indeed have a large home. It was a beautiful four thousand square feet two-story split–level ranch that sat at the end of a cul-de-sac. There was not a blade of grass out of place on the lawn; every inch of the yard was maintained. It was the first thing I noticed when we arrived. I thought to myself *if the outside looks this nice, I would be too afraid to touch or sit on anything on the inside.*

Murphy and I settled into the mauve-colored bedroom we were assigned, uncertain if we should sit on the bed or just stand in the center of the room. It was nicely decorated with a sleigh bed and matching armoire that held a large television and extra linens.

Everything was perfect and in place. From the family portraits to the crown molding, it was as if the room was part of a movie set.

Riley's parents came upstairs to introduce themselves; they were a well-dressed, lovely middle-aged couple. Mr. Jones wore navy blue slacks with black pinstripes, a brown leather belt that matched his leather loafers and a white button-down dress shirt with the initials EDJ on the cuffs. Sprinkles of grey showed on the sides of his freshly cut hair and in his well-groomed beard. His Oliver Peoples glasses gave him a handsome professional appearance.

Mrs. Jones had her arm laced through his with her right wrist gently resting across it. She was equally impeccably dressed in a grey linen dress that zipped in the back. It reminded me of what you would see a TV lawyer wear. A bob-styled haircut accented her tiny heart-shaped face. If by chance you didn't take notice of her perfect skin and her curves in the fitted dress, you surely didn't miss the Rolex Oyster and the pair of six-inch black heels she stood in.

"Hi girls, we are Mr. and Mrs. Jones. I am Peter, and this is my wife, Karen. We're so grateful to have you with us."

"Thank you for having us. I'm Kennedy."

"And I'm Murphy."

"Riley has told us so much about you young ladies."

We stood there perplexed as to why Riley would be talking to his parents about us. I hoped the conversation was not about to go in the direction of why we weren't dating Riley. The look on Murphy's face said she was thinking the same.

"He did say that you girls were pretty; so, where are you from?" Mrs. Jones asked.

"I'm from Florida," I said, hoping she would not pry too much. I do believe I would have lied; I would have named any city other than the small town where I was raised.

"I'm from New York but my parents live in Fresno. We'll be making our way there to see them," Murphy chimed in.

"Fresno is a wonderful city, and it has been a while since our last Florida vacation."

"We recently had the best trip to Florida." Murphy and I chuckled at the thought my statement brought.

"How do you like college, and what's your major?"

"Journalism. Sports journalism to be exact," said Murphy.

"And you?" redirecting her question toward me.

"Business. I plan to be an entrepreneur."

Just as Mrs. Jones was about to speak, Mr. Jones interrupted. During the conversation, he'd taken a seat on the dresser. His feet dangled as he smiled.

"Honey, we have ample time to get to know them. Let's allow them to get settled. I'm sure they are exhausted and want to freshen up."

We thanked them again for allowing us to stay with them, and after a quick catnap and shower, we went down for dinner.

During dinner, we soon learned that Riley had painted his parents in a different light from what I observed. If they were conservative, they were absolutely fabulous. They did have money, but they were not snooty or brash with it; in fact, they were far from it. During dinner they told us that Mr. Jones was an entrepreneur and Mrs. Jones was a professor at an HBCU. They sent Riley to Philander Smith with the hope that he would return to take over his father's business. We must have made a great impression because they said it was courageous of us to take advantage of all that life was offering us. They suggested that we see as much of the world as possible and have as much fun as we could handle safely while we were doing it. However, his father could not believe Riley wasn't dating one of us.

"That boy must be crazy. Why is he dating that girl instead of one of you?" Mr. Jones shook his head.

For some reason, Riley's parents really did not like his girlfriend. She was a country girl from Helena, Arkansas who doted on and obeyed Riley's every word. It was as if she did not have an identity. And it did not sit well with them.

After breakfast one morning, Mr. Jones looked at us without any emotion and unloaded. "She is a tag-along. Her whole existence is Riley, and at some point in his life a woman like that will not be there for him. He will take from her until everything that makes him a trusting, reputable man is destroyed. His kids will hate him, his business partners will not respect him and she will have stopped loving him. I know my son, and that boy does not need a timid woman in his life."

Shocked at what we were hearing, Murphy and I understood exactly what he was saying; we understood that his son would need someone to challenge him yet hold him accountable.

However, truth be told, Riley was not our type. Sure, he was handsome and smart, but neither one of us was looking to break up a relationship. We were more than content with being friends.

We were determined to party every night in California, especially in LA. We called Malik. He told us he had plans for us every night, starting with hitting some of the best clubs and parties in the city. First, we were on a roof top downtown, then in a warehouse in an industrial area. The next night we were on the set of a music video. Every place we went, he had us meeting celebrities, and with every party he would give us instructions on how to dress and how to transform ourselves to fit the occasion. And each party found us meeting new people who would invite us to other parties.

California has such a different vibe than Florida; everyone was beautiful and fashionable but in a different way. It seemed to be more sophisticated. As such, we were never at a shortage of things to do.

After staying with Riley's parents for a few days, it was time to stay a couple of days with Cam's parents, but we were going to miss the Joneses. Especially Riley's younger sister who had hung around us the entire time we were in the house. She would ask so many questions while we put on our makeup to go out. She loved staying up late to see what we were wearing.

We packed our bags and said our goodbyes to Mr. and Mrs. Jones who told us they had really enjoyed having us around.

Cam's parents lived in Compton; they were polite and conservative also, but they were bougie. I guess there is nothing wrong with trying to better one's status, but it was nothing like being at Riley's parents' home. The Joneses were comfortable in their wealth; here it seemed stilted, somehow forced.

Every evening we had to be in place for family dinner. Family dinner meant tablecloths and meaningful conversation, always led by Cam's stepmother. It was visibly clear that no one enjoyed her topics; even her husband rushed through his answers when he spoke.

She was pushy, and we were sick of her after the first night. Cam's mother said she was concerned about our safety and all the partying we were planning to do. She had a completely different philosophy about life and how it should be lived, far different from the Joneses. They were cautious but easygoing. Then there was Cam's mom who seemed willing to give up so much of her life to her fears.

This was too much for us, so to ease the warden's ways, we invited Cam to hang out with us, knowing that the parties we were going to were not his type of thing.

Cam wanted to be a thug, but we knew he was soft. I'm sure all of Compton knew he was soft. He was too educated, and his parents were not going to have any of that. He could only try that thug crap in Arkansas.

We finally convinced his mom that there was no need for us to wake them when we came in. You guessed right! She wanted to give us a curfew! And she wanted to get up to unlock the door when we returned! She finally gave in and allowed us to have a key.

When we called Malik for our plans for that night, we already kind of knew what we were going to do. Of course, we went to a club, and we had no plans of seeing Cam until it was time to leave. That was fine with him. It gave him time to hang around with his boys.

Out of all the parties we had ever gone to, this was by far the best one. Malik had arranged VIP services at Prince's nightclub, Glam Slam. It was the hottest place to be in the early '90s. There was already a line when we arrived, so we were hesitant to bypass everyone. We told the guy at the door that we were guests of Malik. The large man simply stared at us with his intense face before telling us to wait a moment. He called someone on a radio. A few moments passed before a gentleman appeared wearing a well-tailored suit and a huge smile. With a European accent, he greeted us.

"Kennedy and Murphy, we are so happy to have you. Welcome to Glam Slam!" As he escorted us through the club, our minds were blown away by what was happening around us. He told us that we had two options for accommodations available to us: we could have a table by the stage, but he preferred we have the table in VIP with security. Of course, we just had to know what this VIP security detail meant.

Murphy and I spoke in unison, "VIP, please!"

He escorted us upstairs and sat us at our table. He told us everything had been taken care of. Our table gave us a perfect view of the club—the dancefloor, the bar, the tables, the stage, staff moving back and forth as they performed their duties, and security guards at every corner, doorway and hallway.

"Kennedy, don't look, but that's Magic Johnson behind you." Murphy's voice was sort of a squealing whisper.

"Well, don't look either, but Carmen Electra is sitting to your right."

Her head instantly swiveled.

"I said don't look!" We leaned in and tried to suppress our schoolgirl giggles.

"Ok, I am a mature woman. I can handle a few celebrities," she said, then put her hand over her mouth and giggled some more.

Below us was a sea of well-dressed people partying like it was their last party. The noise was a crush of music, conversation and laughter. We didn't warrant much any attention from anyone, but we couldn't have cared less.

Malik had gone over the top for us, and it took all we had to contain our excitement. Murphy and I danced at our table, but a part of us wanted to be downstairs in the mix of everything. Unable to hold our urge to let loose, we waved a security person over and asked him to take us downstairs. He raised his hand only slightly and three huge bodyguards appeared who made a path through the crowd for us. Once we got to the stage, one of them leaned down and asked, "Would you like to dance on the stage?"

Before Murphy could answer, I shouted to him, "No, we want to dance on that!" pointing at the large speaker on the side of the stage.

"You got it!" He walked us on stage and lifted us onto the speaker. We were in our element, and it didn't take long before the crowd was cheering us. A spotlight hit us and something triggered in me. I became transformed back into a 14K. I gave them a full show with Murphy following my every lead. The DJ stopped playing his normal mix for the crowd and for twenty minutes he mixed a set just for the two of us. The crowd was loving every minute of it, they cheered and shouted for us as if we were a new up-and-coming duet.

Once we finished, the bodyguards politely helped us from the stage and escorted us back to VIP to the whispers of, "Who was that? Who are they?"

To our surprise, Murphy's friend from Bell Biv DeVoe came rushing over.

"Murphy, Kennedy, I couldn't believe my eyes when I saw you on the stage! I should have known; out of all the people I know it would be you two I run into out here in California. Damn! Look at you two, you're the hottest things in here!"

We were happy to see someone we knew. Our evening was turning into something spectacular, and it was about to get better. Murphy's friend lit a joint and passed it to us. The aroma of the bud circled and tingled my nose when I hit it. I let out a smoker's cough and passed the spliff to Murphy.

"I'm going to another party when I leave here. You guys have to come!"

"What party? Whose party?" Murphy replied.

"I can't tell you whose party it is. All I can say is he is famous, and you do not want to miss this opportunity! It will be starting soon, so get your last dance in if you want to go."

I could not believe how the evening was playing out. The weed had us ready to continue with whatever the night had in store. One thirty in the morning was quickly approaching, but the decision to leave a club--a Prince club that was banging at that--to go to another party was a no brainer this time. Could it really get any better than this?

"Everyone knows you don't leave a good party in search of a party," Murphy looked at me confused. But the decision was made.

"Let's go, but we have to let Cam know what we're doing," I replied.

"Well, do it quickly because car service is on its way to get us; did I mention that you can't drive there? You can only go by his car service."

"No, you didn't mention that."

After a brief meet-up with Cam, we were on our way. The three of us sipped on complimentary champagne in the back of the car. eagerly anticipating what was sure to be an unforgettable night.

Murphy's friend would not tell us who was hosting the event; he only would say that he was a famous comedian turned actor. But it didn't matter to me; I was prepared for anything.

The car climbed the winding streets of the Hollywood hills before arriving at a house overlooking the city. You could not tell there was a party taking place from the outside. In fact, the front of the house had a very small footprint. The only sign of an event was the ten or more service vehicles perfectly lined up just inside of the gate. For the first time in my life, I felt nervous about what I was about to do. I was so nervous I needed to hit a joint again to try and settle myself.

The entrance was a large glass door that opened to an opulent courtyard that could have been the size of the average person's home. The courtyard was completely empty of people. Everything in it was neatly in place as if someone had given a whole lot of thought and planning about where things should be placed. The highlight of the palatial courtyard was a twelve-foot beautifully manicured olive tree being illuminated by Tiffany-blue lighting. If I weren't allowed to take another step on the property, I would have been content right where I stood.

Still in awe of the luxurious courtyard, a massive guy appeared from a second set of doors that led to the main house. He greeted us with a welcome and ushered us in. Murphy and I stood frozen. What had appeared to be an average sized Hollywood hills home on the outside blew up to a massive mansion on the inside.

There were beautiful women everywhere. There were celebrities, entertainers and athletes. And it was likely that if the host was an entertainer and actor, some of these people were industry insiders.

I thought that if you had any type of fame or Hollywood career you were at this party.

Just as we pulled it together and managed to look like we belonged, over walked one of the members of Bell Biv DeVoe. Giving Murphy's friend a hug, he turned his attention toward us. "I remember you two. I think we had dinner together."

With a joint hanging from his lips, he mumbled the words, "Let me show you around, but first let's get you drinks!"

On our way to the bar, we just took it all in. Girls danced; countless celebrities held court telling stories to enthralled listeners; this party was sick. He showed the three of us around, periodically introducing us to various people he thought we might be interested in meeting.

In mid-conversation with a basketball player for the Clippers, he snapped his fingers and turned toward me. "That's it, now I know who you remind me of. You resemble Naomi Campbell, you're just lighter!"

"Yea, I get that a lot."

I was always a bit uncomfortable when people remarked on my looks or my resemblance to Naomi, so I quickly turned the conversation back to completing the house tour.

We were headed downstairs to the pool when I noticed the host of the number one late-night show. The same host who embraced urban talent. It was the same host who was known for pointing his finger. He sat in the corner playing a handheld video game. Then it began to dawn on us whose home we were in, but before either one of us could ask, he told us that was not the host of the party. However, our host and the video gamer were good friends, and it all became suddenly clear.

Before we could say who we thought our party host was, we had made it downstairs to an indoor pool.

"Murphy, are you seeing what I'm seeing, or am I dreaming?"

Nothing could have prepared us for a pool filled with naked people. Murphy's friend and our tour guide gave each other five and a chest bump in approval. The lights were low, and a DJ played this Mediterranean, Ibiza electronic music that complimented the smell of weed, and which obviously had everyone in a party mood.

To the left of the pool was a large dance floor completely covered in foam. Entangled naked bodies danced uninhibited on the dance floor. Puffs of foam clouds periodically floated up before bursting onto the ceiling, exposing beautifully sculptured naked torsos. Just to the right of the pool were cabanas with sheer curtains on the front of them. Each cabana had couples clearly having sex; some had several couples, others had groups in them. Whatever barrier or privacy the curtains were supposed to provide was nonexistent; you could see right through them. Some people did just that; they stood there taking in the entertainment each cabana provided in a gross display of voyeurism.

I didn't know whether I was thrilled or appalled, but I went with the flow and didn't express my any words or opinions. I was slightly intimidated. As wild as I thought I had been over the past few months, this was so over the top that I had to take a minute to wrap my head around it. So this was the Hollywood set.

Once again, our tour guide broke my trance. "Let me finish showing you around. Besides, the rule this evening is if you're at the pool you must be naked."

Like twins who are always on the same wavelength and have the same thoughts, Murphy and I chimed in, "Let's see the rest of the party."

We made our way back upstairs occasionally brushing remnants of foam from our attire. Astonished by what we'd just seen, we made it back to the second floor then went up to the third floor. And if we thought we saw beautiful women on the other two floors; this one was something to behold.

"That was the B team downstairs. The A-team is on a whole different level, physically, visually and mentally."

The three of us were amazed: me, Murphy, and her friend. We could not believe the type of beauty around us. These people were exotic. They all looked like imported gods and goddesses. They all had perfect skin, perfect hair, perfect smiles and teeth, perfect eyes, perfect figures, and what appeared to be the most perfectly designed and executed clothes. I felt like I was on a movie set. Let us just say everything about every single one of the men and women on the third floor appeared perfect, almost to the point where they didn't seem real. I have been called beautiful my entire life, and I'm constantly being told that I resemble Naomi Campbell. I had seen the reaction by many to Murphy's Dominican-Nigerian beauty. But up here? Our beauty fell short by a mile. We were amateurs, kids playing at being exotic grownups, thinking we were all that because the men who complimented us had never seen what we were seeing now. I now considered myself only average pretty. And that was ok with me, but it sure was an eye-opener.

Perhaps this was what other women felt when they were around us. It was an insecurity based on society's adoration of beauty, but we did not continue doubting our looks for long.

Our attention was drawn from the women to the sound of music coming from a room down the hall. Curiosity got the best of us, so we made our way to the room and peeked in. And low and behold there he was--the host. Mr. Saturday Night Live, the comedian-actor with the distinctive laugh. He sat on the floor of this room playing the guitar and singing into a mic. On the other side of the room was a wall of speakers. He acknowledged us with a small smile while he continued to sing and play. It was not long before he and our tour guide started singing together and the room began to fill with people eager to take in the impromptu performance.

The whole thing was surreal. *No one is going to believe this.* If everyone at college thought our party was something, just wait until they heard about this evening. As far as parties are concerned, ours was a tiny fish in the big sea.

After a few more drinks, dances and conversations with athletes running their charming pickup game on us, the sun began to rise. The time had come for us to call it a night.

The car service arrived at Cam's parents' home at the perfect time. We had just missed them; they had already left for early morning service. Murphy and I were more than happy to have avoided a morning lecture from them. I'm sure there would have been nothing we could have said to make our actions okay in their eyes. Unless they were impressed by celebrities, which I have a tiny feeling they might have been.

We had been up the entire night and the weed and alcohol made us feel more tired than we might have been, but we were eager to get going. We packed quickly and said goodbye to Cam before hitting the road to Murphy's parents' house.

Murphy's parents were thrilled to see us when got to Fresno. Her mother had prepared more food than we could have ever eaten. In fact, the whole time we were there, all we did was eat. We already knew there would not be much to do there, so relaxing and preparing for the long drive back home was all we had on the agenda. We made sure to take full advantage of it.

California had been the perfect host; she had graciously given me the best Christmas break ever.

ROLLERBLADING IN BUCKHEAD

For as long as I can remember, I have felt like an anomaly. When I lived in a small town, I looked like all the other kids, but I felt like the odd man out. When I took part in dance and baton, I was easily singled out being the only black girl. Even when I was around my relatives, I was the anomaly because I was tall and light skinned. All the years I was in college, I felt like the anomaly for all those reasons. Sometimes being the anomaly makes you not care about much, it makes you keep your heart close, and you often act recklessly. Being the anomaly can really mess with your head.

Greyson and Kylie brought in a late lunch for me and the makeup team. The car service would be picking us up at seven o'clock, which was two and a half hours away. That was enough time for us to finish with hair and makeup, get dressed, and for me to finish sharing my story with Kylie and Greyson. I continued.

After Christmas break, school flew by for us. Before we knew it, it was Spring break. Murphy and I, along with a couple of our friends, spent time in Daytona Beach for Black Beach Week. Then we darted off to Miami and Key West.

School breaks were just as challenging for me as the holidays. Like I said earlier, I had a thing about spending lengthy periods of time alone; I always have. They always made me really miss my mother, which filled me with loneliness. Besides, I did not have any family members to visit, or should I say anyone who made me feel like family.

I called my godsister, Lynn, at Spellman to see what her plans were for the summer break. She told me that she was attending their family reunion. I could hear the excitement in her voice when she spoke. Lynn was so excited because this year's reunion was being held in Washington, DC. After checking with her parents, I was all too thrilled to be on board with joining them.

Lynn's parents had taken me in as their godchild after my mother's death. I will never forget the day my mother passed. Lynn and her sister, Sonya, came to my house and spent the entire day with me; they consoled me during my hurt. They comforted me every day. I do not know what I would have done if not for them.

With plans for the summer, I now had life in me. The drive to Atlanta was peaceful. I had become a pro at taking long drives even if it meant doing it alone. Lynn and I had a few hours to catch up before her mother and Sonya were to arrive from Florida. We wanted to take advantage of it because once Sonya arrived, we knew she would take over the conversation and want to be in all our business. Sonya always wanted to hear about what was happening at college, and somehow, she knew just when to use whatever information she had gotten to blackmail Lynn and me. Even though I respected my godmother and she never chastised me for anything I was doing, I didn't want her parenting me because of Sonya's big mouth.

The morning of our drive to DC, we had breakfast at a diner before getting on the road. While having breakfast, I noticed this attractive white guy looking at me. Though I pretended to look away, his staring was persistent. It was not long before Sonya noticed; she didn't miss anything.

"Damn Kennedy, he is all into you." Her comment distracted me just as I locked eyes with him. He was extremely attractive: tall with black hair, blue eyes, red cherry lips, and from what I could tell, a well-muscled body. Without hesitation he came over and introduced himself as Jonathan in front of Lynn, Sonya, and my godmother. My heart dropped; it is one thing to meet a man when you are with your girls, but it's just uncomfortable to meet one when you are with your godmother. I got up from the table, excused myself and had a quick conversation with Jonathan. I told him that it was bold of him to come over to a table of four black women, but it was very impressive.

"Opportunity isn't always comfortable!" he stated, like he could read my mind. Did I look that uncomfortable?

I told him to give me his number and I would call him once our trip to DC ended. He was really cute, and I made a note to call him once I returned.

On the drive to DC, we had fun talking about old times. Lynn and her family had had the opportunity to meet my ex-boyfriend, Chase, before my mother passed. We reminisced on how he used to tell these incredible stories, going on double dates, and of course how the three of us used to go to all the parties together.

Sonya was older than Lynn and me, but I often found her to be intriguing and cool despite the fact that she was in the habit of taking advantage of us at almost any opportunity. Sonya was the person that was always thinking two steps ahead of everyone. She was always working an angle, and you usually did not know it until it was too late. And for that reason, we always tried to leave her out of some of our business. Sonya wanted to know everything about us. She would ask so many questions and then try to tell us how we should be doing things. She was extremely bossy; she was the typical older sibling who thought they knew everything. But Sonya had more hustle than anyone I knew; Sonya had game.

It was the first time I'd seen her since the incident in Orlando involving the promoter and the missing—or shall I say stolen--money. That was a total mess. I prepared myself for that story to come up, but to my surprise, she never mentioned it. I guess there were still some things she didn't want her mother to know.

We had stopped to stretch our legs and to get some dinner at a fast-food restaurant when Lynn and I thought it would be a clever idea to smoke weed behind a tree at the back of the restaurant. We thought we had picked the perfect spot to not be noticed and, like all the times before, we did not want Sonya to know what we were up to. We agreed we would only take a few puffs, get in the car and fall asleep, leaving Sonya to drive. As soon as we got to the car, Sonya saw her opportunity, and she did not waste it. She rushed from the restaurant. "You two bitches have been smoking. I smell it."

It was rare that we could get anything past her. We only had a few moments before my godmother was going to return to the car and the whole trip would be ruined.

"Fifty dollars, I want fifty dollars, or I'm telling Mommy everything."

Lynn and I quickly reached into our purses and gave twenty-five dollars each. We knew Sonya was not playing and would have no problem giving us up, so we didn't hesitate. There was no time for negotiation or pleading our case. Lynn pictured herself the good girl of the family. She was the one who went to college, and even though their parents did not show favoritism with them, Sonya wouldn't miss the chance to remind them that Lynn wasn't as good as they thought.

The family reunion was planned very well; they had thought of everything. The first day included a meet-and-greet in the penthouse of a very nice hotel. Every three years this large extended family came from all over the country to attend the event. During the day, we went on tours throughout the city, and at night we all went out to party together.

On the final night, there was a formal celebratory banquet during which college scholarships were handed out. Upon my inquiry, I was told that the adults from each individual family collected, saved and donated money, which was then pooled with the other families to create small scholarships for anyone who wanted to attend college and who had shown their commitment to getting good grades.

This was my first family reunion, so I did not know what to expect, but it turned out to be much more than I could have imagined a family event would be.

Once the reunion ended, we went to New Jersey and stayed there for a few days. Lynn's and Sonya's father still worked and lived in New Jersey. He was close to retiring and had begun the process of transitioning his family to Florida. He loved his girls, so the opportunity to have a few extra days with his family just could not be passed up. This was my first time visiting New Jersey, and I was thrilled at the opportunity to see where they grew up and to meet some of Lynn's childhood friends.

Once we returned to Atlanta, I called Jonathan, and after a few phone conversations we agreed to a lunch date. With all the excitement from the reunion I had not thought much about him, but I didn't have much going on for the rest of the summer so I thought he would be a handsome distraction.

Jonathan was a trust fund kid. With his parents' approval, he had forgone his senior year at Georgia Tech and was interning and studying under a wealthy Atlanta businessman.

The way he saw it; he was learning more interning with this man than he would be learning in college. He was learning a specific skill for a career in market research for the Asian stock market, and he was learning from the best.

Every day, we would hang out in eclectic parts of Atlanta that I had never visited with my friends. We spent a lot of time at the mall shopping and dining at the best restaurants. Lynn could not believe all the money Jonathan was spending on me. If he did not have time for us to go out, we would have fun rollerblading and pretending to play hockey in front of his cottage in Buckhead. I felt like I was living the life I should be living; it was the life I felt I deserved. I did not want to think about going back to college in the fall.

I knew if things continued at the pace they were going; Jonathan would not be pleased with me. I knew I did not want a boyfriend, and as nice as he had been, my heart wasn't telling me he was the one. It did not matter how blue his eyes were or how broad his shoulders were or how much money he had. In fact, he was everything a woman would want in a man. Handsome, smart, attentive, caring, funny, and he had the means to provide...but without the one element that overcomes everything, none of that mattered.

Jonathan and I had come to an understanding of our friendship, which worked out well for me when he needed to travel to Asia. This freed up my final two weeks so I could spend them with Lynn without distractions. Lynn and I brought out the best in each other; we constantly encouraged and motivated each other. We pushed each other and did not pass judgment when one of us made mistakes. It was a true friendship.

During my visit, my car developed mechanical problems. I wasn't too concerned at first; I simply contacted my attorney to receive an advance of my monthly income. I had requested advances before, so I didn't give it much thought. However, the beginning of the fall semester was less than a week away. There were procedures to be followed in this sort of thing and I was a little concerned about getting it in time. I did get the money, however, but not from where I thought I'd get it.

All my enthusiasm and optimism changed when Murphy called to tell me she wasn't returning to school; she was moving to San Francisco. She was the closest thing to family I had in Little Rock, and school would not be the same without her there.

Things seemed to be falling apart rapidly. First Murphy was not returning and now the car. I hadn't received any money yet, so once the car was repaired, I went to negotiate getting it back from the mechanic, but he was not having any of it. Even after I offered my title and extra money if he allowed me to pay him later, once I got the advance, he refused. I called a cab and waited at a bar and grill across from the auto repair shop. I was disappointed and looking very dejected.

It was taking everything I had not to burst into tears sitting at the bar. What was I going to do?" Time was rapidly running out; I only had a couple of days left before I needed to be back in school. I thought of calling Jonathan but ultimately decided not to. To be honest, I did not want him to think I couldn't solve my problems on my own, even though I know his father was a safety net for him when he found himself in a situation.

It must have been written all over my face because I didn't even notice the older gentleman sitting next to me until he spoke to me. "You look like you could use a drink."

I apologized for not speaking when I first sat beside him.

"Whatever it is, it cannot be that bad!"

I told him about the wonderful summer I was having, and how everything was now falling apart. I told him about Murphy, the car and missing the semester and how I wished I had my parents to help me resolve the problems. The conversation was small talk to kill time while I waited for the cab. At one point I did not think he was paying attention to what I was saying. I am sure having a stranger share all her problems with him wasn't what he had hoped for.

My cab arrived; I paid the tab and collected my purse. I thanked him for being a kind ear to my issues and turned to leave.

"Kennedy come by my office tomorrow. I think I can help."

I took his card and said goodbye, thanking him again. The entire time I sat waiting for the cab, I was so focused on what I had going on, I'm ashamed to say I didn't remember his name or very much about the gentleman, to say the least. But the following day Lynn and I arrived in a cab at the address on the business card.

We stood in the parking lot in disbelief, surprise and delight. After double-checking the address to make sure we were at the right location, we approached the receptionist. Before we headed to the elevator, I leaned into the receptionist and asked who the gentleman on the card was. I will never forget the look on her face when she told me he was the owner of the record label whose offices were in this building. The entire building. When we got to his office, his secretary told us that he was not in, but he had left a package for me.

Once we returned to the car with the package, I opened the envelope; inside was a note that read: "Kennedy, the Lord spoke to me yesterday when we met. There is something spectacular about you. He moved me to look after you. I have contacted the auto shop on your behalf and taken care of the repairs. Your car is ready for you to pick it up. Good luck with school."

Wow! I was amazed that something like this could even happen. Did people really do that? It was then that I remembered how I'd cried and talked about wanting to help others when we were gathered around Thanksgiving dinner. This is the kind of thing I knew was right. I was on the receiving end of great and unselfish generosity, and one day I would be on the giving end.

I immediately picked up my car and returned to his office the following day with a copy of the invoice and receipt along with a thank you card and balloons. I knew it was cheesy, especially for someone in his position, but I couldn't think of any other way to say thank you. I asked if I could see the gentleman and handed the receptionist the card, receipt, and balloons. She informed me that he was not in.

"What is your name?"

"Kennedy, ma'am."

"I don't know how or where you met him, but he is only in this office twice a year, and it's usually only for an hour or two. He is a very private gentleman and rarely says much."

"Will these get to him," I asked.

She nodded and smiled. I thanked her and entered the elevator, once again in disbelief. What were the odds that he and I would be in the same bar and grill at the same time, and just at the exact moment I needed the helping hand of an angel?

I returned to Little Rock to finish the semester without Murphy, but everything was different now. She was still paying her part of the rent and did visit from time to time, but for me, Little Rock was not the same.

GRUMPY CATERPILLAR

Of all the memories and moments with my mother, my favorite was the nighttime snack routine we shared. It began when I was in elementary school sometime after my father Earl died, and it continued until I left for college. Every night around nine o'clock, I would snuggle up in her bed and she would bring us a snack. Most evenings it was orange slices or apple wedges, but sometimes she would have ice cream or sherbet. This was our bonding time. We would lie on the bed together and eat our snack watching television, and other times we would simply talk while we ate or read the Bible. However, it did not matter to me what we did, it was our time.

I had a perfectly decorated room of my own that any kid would want, but every night I would fall asleep next to my mother after our snack in her bed. It must have been what we both needed because she never kicked me out of bed or placed me in my bed once I fell asleep.

Regardless of what was happening in my life, it was the only time I truly felt at peace.

I wish I could lay in the bed and share orange slices with my mother again.

As the hair and makeup team completed their work and began packing up their equipment, I pulled Kylie over to the couch on the opposite side of the bedroom to get out of their way. Greyson helped take their things to the car to expedite the process.

I gently touched Kylie's newly straightened hair and gazed at her. I longed for my mother to gaze at me the way she used to.

"Sweetie, you know how I love to have nighttime snacks with you?"

"Yeah, Mom! I love it, too. I still don't think Dad knows we do it," she peeked toward the door making sure her father hadn't overheard us.

"He has no idea," I snickered. "I never told you this, but my mom and I used to have nighttime snacks together. Besides shopping, it was one of our favorite things to do together."

I had returned to Philander Smith for my senior year completely unmotivated and still not knowing the direction my life would take. School and the house had become boring without my best friend, Murphy, being there. I had gone to visit her in San Francisco, and we had a wonderful time revisiting our tour with the band and reminiscing about the crazy things we'd done together. Naturally, we were both sorry when it came time for me to leave, but it was time for me to get focused. All my talk about wanting to help others would amount to nothing if I couldn't even make it through college. And on top of that, I felt as though I was currently a disappointment to my mother, Mary, and my dad, Earl. I knew that if they were alive, they would find a way to make me feel that all my recent actions—my careless and carefree attitude toward school—were okay, but I knew deep down that things had to change.

Chase and I had begun dating again. It started with a few small dates when I returned from San Francisco, but things were beginning to get serious again.

I continued living with my roommates at the house, but I spent a lot more of my time with Chase and Dr. Morgan. I noticed a substantial change in Chase.; He was not as controlling. He had returned to being the Chase I loved when we first met. Perhaps it was because Murphy was not around.

A couple of months had passed, and our dating was the comfortable change that I needed. It gave me the time to relax and reflect on the hectic party life I had been leading.

Sunday dinner was a ritual at Dr. Morgan's home. It was a tradition long before I came to Little Rock, so when I arrived one Sunday to meet there for dinner, I didn't give it any thought when I saw the driveway full of cars. But I was in for a complete surprise!

Chase looked anxious during dinner; he moved nervously through the room unfocused on any of his conversations. Every time I would ask him if things were okay, he would just smile and quickly redirect the topic and walk away, but it was quite obvious there was something on his mind.

Dr. Morgan asked everyone to gather in the formal living room for an announcement. I remember staring at the paneled walls preparing to hear the worst as Chase took his mother's side.

Perhaps she was ill; was I losing a mother once again? Chase began to speak, and my knees trembled as I prepared for what I thought was sure to be life-changing news. When Chase called me forward to stand with them, my heart fluttered with fear. Was Dr. Morgan dying? Did she have cancer like my mother? Those were the only thoughts going through my head as I walked toward him.

The room began to fill with whispers and people speaking under their breath. I stepped close to Chase and took his hand, hoping to give him courage through what I thought was going to be some devastating news. But I was shocked when he dropped to one knee and reached into his blazer pocket to draw out a black velvet ring box. Everything—every thought, every move, every argument–that came before that moment was forgotten.

"Kennedy, will you marry me?"

At that moment, there was no one in the room but Chase and me.

"Yes!" I didn't miss a beat.

His proposal was as much a surprise to me as it was to everyone else. I loved Chase, yet neither one of us was in any hurry to set a wedding date. We both liked the idea of saying we are engaged more than the idea of actually being husband and wife. Once again, I was faced with a life-affecting decision, to be made without the benefit of my mother's advice and wisdom, but I did take solace in knowing my mother had known Chase.

The more I tried to force myself to continue, the more I started to feel like it was time to move on from college. It was the same feeling I had when I attended Bethune Cookman before my mother passed. So, I quietly finished the semester, knowing that it was time for me to go back home to Florida. Something deep down inside was forcing me to go back, and I knew I had to follow that inner voice that had never failed me before.

At the end of the semester, Chase and I packed up the house. My other roommates left to go home, and I planned my return trip home. I had no problem convincing Chase to move to Florida. Our plan was for me to move there, then get one of the rental homes ready for Chase and me to live in once he graduated.

I was nervous and confused about my future. The uncertainty of it made my stomach quiver. Yet despite my uneasy nerves, I felt thrilled and excited about it. I decided to trust the process, so any nagging doubts I might have had about our decision didn't matter at this point. My mother had always told me that there was an anointing on my life, and she had not been the only one to utter those words to me. Those were the words of encouragement I needed to remember to move forward with my decision to marry Chase and move back to Florida.

I remember one time while still in Arkansas there was a blizzard headed for Little Rock, but I did not give it much thought because I was coming up from the southeast, from Florida. I grew up with countless hurricanes hitting Florida. I had seen the destruction they could create. I also recall how we would prepare by boarding up windows, tying down anything outside that could be blown away, and stocking up on things like water and batteries. Then nothing would happen. The hurricane would pass. So maybe this was the reason I did not give much thought to the warning signals that were sitting at the back of my thoughts, of an approaching storm, a big red flag that was trying to get my attention, and that I ignored.

I was working a part-time job at the mall when the announcement was made that the mall was closing, and everyone needed to leave at once. This wasn't my first time seeing snow nor was it my first time commuting in it, however, it was my first time driving in snow. All the prior winters, Chase had done all the driving.

I had no idea at the time how difficult it was to drive in a snowstorm. My car was skittering over the road and the snow was somewhat blinding, obscuring the light traffic around me. Just when I thought, "Okay Kennedy, you got this," the vehicle began to slide uncontrollably. I regained just enough control to pull into the parking lot of a grocery store and immediately broke down.

My nerves and emotions were a wreck. I began to cry uncontrollably, like a teething baby. It must have been loud crying because I did not even notice the gentleman approach my car.

"Is everything okay young lady?"

I rolled the window halfway. "No, it's not."

Between crying like a kid and trying to talk, I told him I was from Florida, it was my first storm, and I didn't know how to drive in it or what to do. He offered to take me home, but he needed to get supplies for the elderly members of the church first. He gathered his supplies and showed me what I would need to get through the storm if I became snowed in. Once he dropped me off at home, he suggested I visit the church he attended.

A few weeks later, I found a seat in the balcony of the packed church. The pastor began preaching and shortly into his sermon, things started to happen. It was what the elders called "the spirit." I remember them saying "the spirit is moving in here." I watched as each member would catch the Holy Ghost and fall to the floor or shout and dance down the aisles.

Once order was restored to the congregation, the pastor stopped and stared at the balcony. He stood there staring for a few minutes before speaking.

"Young lady, you will be happy; the Lord told me you will be happy."

Sitting there, I was not sure who he was speaking too as he continued to stare into the balcony.

"The young lady in white."

The entire congregation turned with curiosity to have a look into the balcony. I turned and looked around before realizing that I was the only one in white. An uneasy feeling came over me. I prayed that the pastor was speaking to anyone but me. I did not want the attention. My heart began to race once I knew that he was indeed talking to me.

"You were anointed in your mother's womb young lady. There is an amazing favor placed over you. You do not have to concern yourself with what troubles you, it is not a part of you."

The pastor was speaking the exact things my mother used to say to me during those evenings eating orange slices.

On my drive to Florida, I decided to travel to Mississippi again to visit my biological sister and brothers. I desperately wanted to see them before going back to Florida because I did not know when I would see them again after that. It had been a couple of years since my last visit. Deep inside of me I felt bad about how different our lives had turned out. It was a sad situation, more like an out of sight out of mind type of thing.

We would try to keep in touch here and there, but it became harder for me after my mother, Mary, died. My biological mother's actions had changed the course of my life. After her death, my siblings lived a much harder life than the one I had in Florida. It wasn't necessarily a bad life for them, but I always felt as though I didn't deserve what I had, what I was given. I felt they deserved to share in what Mary had given me, but my thinking was illogical, flawed. She was not there mother.

When I arrived in Mississippi, they made me feel like a rock star the whole time I was there. They wanted to show me off to all their friends like we were little kids. So, you see, that illogical thinking was only in my mind, not theirs.

"Meet my little sister, isn't she beautiful?" Even during dinner, they told the waiter I was their sister. After dinner, we went to a small juke joint and I bought rounds of drinks all night to celebrate my engagement. They were not used to this nor was the small club. They felt like high rollers, and I enjoyed making them feel that way. I felt guilty for the life that they had, and over time it had become much easier to say I was an only child. No one asked questions when I said that, but if I said I had siblings, it always led to questions I did not want to answer.

The next morning, I hit the road in route to Florida. I had made plans to live with a relative for a few months with the hope of finding employment, getting the tenants moved out and getting the house ready for Chase and me to live in. My cousin, the one I was staying with, was one of my mom's favorite nieces. I remember, when we were kids, how my mom helped her to become stable in her adulthood, so I felt like she would be the perfect person to ask for a favor.

During the drive I reflected over the events of the last few years. I had mostly traveled and partied the entire time and, yeah, there was that getting engaged thing. Just as I started to feel bad about it all, I thought of all the wonderful people I had met, all the angels that had been placed in my life to see me through it all. Then I realized that I was only a semester away from having a degree. No one from my childhood believed I would even go to college let alone be a semester away from a degree. By the time I reached my cousin's home in Florida, I was at peace with my memories.

I leaned back stretching my arms out, running my fingers over my cousin's worn-out leather sofa. With every scratch, dent or lump I imagined what all the couch had witnessed. How many times someone jumped on it, crashed into it, how many times it had been moved and repositioned; yet here it still stood serving its purpose.

I really didn't know what to expect starting over in Orlando, but I was now determined to give it everything that I had, much like the weathered couch.

I thanked God for allowing me to make it to my cousin's home safely. I thanked him for watching over my life and for the new beginning.

I had properties and a couple of businesses; it was how I financially sustained myself in college. All the properties had been rented out, and I had a property manager overseeing them. One of my mother's good friends was managing the businesses. She had put strong people in place to manage the day-to-day operations. My mom also had a great legal team. The same people who once hired her to look after their parent's needs were now part of her legal counsel, and they worked to ensure everything was being handled properly after my mother's death. I told you my mother had courage.

I rarely told anyone about my inheritance, including Dr. Morgan or Chase. I may have mentioned the house I grew up in was being rented out, but that was it. I made every effort to keep my business to myself, especially about my past and being adopted. As far as anyone knew, I was an only child with not much family or income. It was a strategy that I felt I needed in order to survive.

STRONGER

Contemplating my reflection in the mirror, wrapped in a satin robe, and still sitting in the room that the hair and makeup team had just evacuated, I wondered if my mother would make the same choice of giving me up for adoption today as she had then, knowing she would eventually pay with her life at the hands of Phillip, the man who fathered me. It was a question I often thought of. Did she consider the ramifications of adoption knowing Phillip was so volatile? Surely, she had a level of fearlessness that you had to have to take on someone like Phillip. She had to know his past was a clear sign of how far he would go to get revenge against anyone who challenged his authority. And why was she involved with someone like Phillip anyway? From all accounts of what I have heard about my biological mother, I could not come to terms with why she decided to put herself in that position. So many things had to go right for everyone involved to walk away happy. Sometimes I think that if we stopped to think about all the ramifications involved and the potential consequences of the decisions we make, we'd never do anything.

Greyson, Kylie and I moved to the couch as I was making it to the final parts of my story. It was almost time for us to get dressed, and I wanted Kylie to know about how I became the businesswoman I am today and about the first time I met her dad…

I decided to meet with my attorney to transition me into running the business and property management. I had developed a plan to take control of everything. I figured it would be the quickest way for me to grow. Besides, it was mine, and it was time for me to be an adult and not wait for someone to decide what I should or should not do with what was rightfully mine.

The entire time I had been in college, I had someone other than myself managing things for me. I remember once when I returned home, I went to the storage unit that housed all my mother's belongings. A living room set, dining room set, piano, and all the other furniture from our home was stored in that unit. The manager told me that they had auctioned off the contents of the unit. I was furious and started to scream and yell. The manager told me that they had not received payment for the unit, and they had attempted to reach me. Invoices were going to one of my relatives who was to pay for the unit; but they had not made a payment in six months. This was the one task I had forgotten to assign to the managers before moving to Arkansas, and without thinking things through, I asked my cousin. I rushed to the relative's house prepared to face the thief. My mind raced with the thought that I had lost all my mother's heirlooms. For over two hours, I sat in her driveway waiting for her to show up.

"Kennedy, when did you get in town?" She tried to get in the door quickly before I could rush her.

"That's not important. Why didn't you pay for the storage unit? You were supposed to pay the bill for me." I got up in her face.

"I never agreed to pay your bills. I don't have time to handle your responsibilities for you."

"Why didn't you just tell me that instead of ignoring the bill to the point where now all my mother's possessions were sold at auction?"

We went back and forth exchanging obscenities and threats before we both calmed down.

"Where is my money? I want my money!" My arms were flailing everywhere.

Leaving me standing on the porch, she went into the house and returned with six months of checks for the storage unit and told me to leave.

I knew it was my responsibility to make sure things were done, but losing my mother made things hurt like hell. She could have at least warned me that she wasn't going to send the checks.

The attorney told me he could have the property management documents ready in a month or so, but the business would require forms to be filed with the state which could take a little longer.

Living with my cousin was nice. However, I tried to stay away as much as possible. She was a mother with three kids, two in high school and one in middle school, so I wanted to give them space. The middle school kid warmed up to me right away; he always wanted to hang out with me. He was always asking questions about college. Which school did I like better? What were the girls like? Was it hard to get in? How much homework do they give you?

His inquisitiveness was cute. But I had to tell him, "Look, cousin, you have to get a haircut if you want the girls in college to talk to you."

"My mom won't take me to the barber. I mean, she's too busy."

"Wow, I didn't realize just how busy your mom is, with you kids and all. Why don't I take you now? Would you like that?"

He beamed from ear to ear. He was so handsome once I took him to get his haircut. I think he smiled all the way home.

To keep me from getting bored and distracted from my plan and Chase, I got a part-time job at Macy's. It was my way of staying focused until things fell into place. Sonya worked for Macy's, so she spoke to her supervisor on my behalf, and I was hired quickly. Sonya had started living with her mother so that she would not be alone until her father fully retired from his job in New Jersey. She still had that New Jersey hustle, she still talked loud and fast; sometimes it was so fast I found it difficult to understand her. Sonya would curse you out in a minute even though she was beautiful, and she dressed like a movie star. I often thought to myself, *how could this beautiful well-dressed woman be speaking to me like this?*

Seeing Sonya, one would know that she wasn't from Florida. Don't get me wrong, there are lots of women from Florida or from other places who dressed very well, but Sonya looked completely different and you noticed it right away. She had a look that was polished. It was astonishing how she always looked complete. Her hair, makeup, clothes, accessories, and perfume were always spot on. Even the way she moved and spoke was polished. Until she started cursing you out.

Sonya was deeply into fashion and running game on guys. I could not keep up with her when it came to either one and I was not about to try. That was a contest I wanted no part of. I had to be myself. She did not go to college like her sister, but she had a degree in street smarts, and watching her made me realize I needed to have a little of that to survive in this world.

At this point, I considered myself well-rounded. I had seen and done a lot in my young life. Things people would give their first born to have experienced, and things some people don't have to endure until they've lived a long life. The grief and tragedy, the extreme highs, the friendships and lovers, the loss and wisdom. The past few years had been centered on college, and I had spent a lot of it partying and traveling, but I don't know what I expected of Orlando.

Orlando had its share of young professionals, and the city was surely growing. There was a university there, defense contractors made it their base, and it had an international airport, but there was also a lot of partying and clubbing taking place. Some people had average jobs, and some had professional careers, but once you were inside a club, with the lights and the music, you couldn't tell the difference. It was the great leveler.

What did I expect from Orlando? I guess I thought I would suddenly become an adult and do what I thought adults did, which turned out to be the same thing I was doing in college. The only difference was people had traded college for a job or career. They worked to pay their mortgage, rent or car note, they worked to take a vacation, they worked to save for their retirement, they worked until they figured out what they wanted to do with their life, and they partied to forget about work. They partied because they no longer had the freedom they once had before they started trading their time for money.

A part of me was disappointed once I figured this out. I envisioned being an adult so differently. I never noticed that my mother worked for these same reasons. She didn't work to party, it was all about the church with her, but surely, she was working for a mortgage and me.

It had been a slow day at Macy's when Sonya's friend, Deco, showed up. Everyone came alive once he arrived, like a celebrity had come into the store. Clerks and managers came to greet him as he shopped throughout the store.

I had met Deco about five or six years prior when I was still in high school; one of my friends had a huge crush on him. Deco was a fashion icon in Orlando, and he always looked like he was dressed for a fashion show. He was doing things with fashion that were way ahead of anyone else, and no guy dressed remotely close to that. He would shop at thrift stores for hours buying the oddest things, then deconstruct and reconstruct them into unique attire.

Deco was talented and versatile, and his personality matched his eccentric appearance. Everyone knew him, and he made you feel as if you were his best friend, even if you had just met him. Deco and Sonya had become close, so once he showed up to the store, they were inseparable. Before he left, he invited us to what he promised would be an outstanding lunch.

The following day, Sonya and I were off to meet him. On our way, Sonya had me hyped up on what was in store for us. She was a great cook, so I figured if she was that excited, this was going to be outstanding.

As we got close to Deco's place, we noticed this guy walking in the direction we were headed.

"That's Greyson! Stop the car!"

I quickly pulled over and Sonya stuck her head out the window and called to him. Greyson removed his sunglasses and headphones, and we waited for him to catch up to us.

"Hey Sonya, how are you? I didn't recognize the car."

"Hi, Greyson, where are you going?"

"I'm on my way to Deco's."

"So are we. Hop in. We can ride together."

"Greyson, this is Kennedy. Kennedy, this is Greyson."

A few moments later, we arrived at Deco's. The front door flew open and there was Deco, waiting at the door smiling like a greeter at a restaurant. He even had the towel over his arm like a waiter.

"I hope y'all are hungry?"

Greyson began to laugh and shake his head. All I knew was I was hungry and excited to see what awaited us.

"I see you ladies found my boy."

The lunch was designed more for us to hang out and talk, so it was not long before Sonya and Deco started sharing the craziest stories. One thing about Sonya, she is very funny, and she can make you laugh nonstop. Deco and Sonya both talked fast as they exchanged adventures and parables, I tried to keep up with the conversation but settled on just sipping the wine. Finally, Deco returned from the kitchen with a casserole dish.

"Lunch is ready."

Greyson began to laugh again. "I'm good, I'm not hungry." He had taken a seat on the couch away from most of the conversation. He read a magazine as if he were completely disinterested in anything in the room.

I recall thinking that was weird. Why did he keep laughing at the oddest times? That was before we opened the casserole dish. Staring into the dish, I thought, *apparently an outstanding lunch means Hamburger Helper.*

GREYSON DAVENPORT

While growing up, my mom never spent a lot of time lecturing me. She did, however, always give lessons and examples, little talks or pieces of advice. It was never a full-blown sit-down lecture about a subject; it was more like in-the-moment nuggets of information. As a child I never understood why I would think things like, *why is she telling me this* or *what is she talking about?*

For example, if we were in the car and she saw a young girl kissing a boy while we were passing the apartments or school, she would ask me how I thought the world viewed what they were doing, and then she would get started.

I remember once at dinner, out of nowhere she looked at me and said, "Kennedy, the character of a man isn't determined by how much money he earns or his title, and certainly the most handsome man on the outside isn't always the most handsome."

As I grew older, she began to give little hints about relationships. She would say things like, "You never want to be unnoticed sweetheart. A woman wants to be noticed by her man, and you always want to know you mean something to him. You have to mean just as much to him as his money does!" At the time, that bit of childhood information sort of went over my head, in one ear and out the other as they say, but over the years, it became invaluable.

Deco was back at Macy's, and once again he had the employees in the palms of his hands. All the single saleswomen fawned over him, batting their eyes and kissing him. I said hello as he passed.

"We have to get together again. I will cook." Deco was serious.

I just laughed and watched as Deco whisked down the aisle in search of deals.

"Can you help me, Kennedy?'

"Hi, Greyson, I didn't know you were here. Are you with Deco?"

"Yes, but he is on a whole new level when he is in search of things. I usually just stand back and let him go. Can you help me with this? I need a belt."

"Sure, I can ring you up."

Greyson had never said much of anything to me. We had never had a conversation, and he had never tried to talk to me, so I was shocked when he asked me for my phone number. I was taken off guard and before I realized what I was saying, I said no. He took the rejection like a gentleman, wished me a great day and thanked me for the service before handing me his business card and walking away. I don't remember if I regretted saying no at the time, but the final outcome is obvious.

"I can't wait to hear how that all played out," said Kylie as we finished with the final details of the story before getting dressed.

It had been one of those days that you just simply wanted to get behind you. It was not because something was going wrong nor were things going particularly right. The whole week had just slowly been dragging along. I needed a breakthrough or something. The completion of the business transfers for my mom's properties continuously played in the back of my head, plus the idea of moving back into my childhood home was starting to sink in. When I left for college, I had vowed that I would never return, and when my mother, Mary, passed, I really didn't have a reason to return.

Every day after work, I would take these long drives to try and clear my head. One day I would go to Daytona to walk the beach, another day I'd drive to Cape Canaveral, my favorite getaway, and just sit and think. It offered the most seclusion. There were never many people there, especially young people, so I knew the chances of someone wanting to talk or hit on me were slim. Depending on when you got there, it was like having a whole beach to yourself. I loved the sand dunes and salty air, and the sound of the waves washing ashore always put me at peace. It was always the perfect place for me to escape and forget about my troubles.

One particular Friday night, I decided to go to a local hotel lounge to pass some time listening to easy music and sipping a drink. The lounge was filled with both locals and hotel guests. A promoter was sponsoring a Hennessey Meet-and-Greet during happy hour. I had promised myself earlier in the week that I wasn't going to go, but this entire week had gotten the best of me, so at the last minute I had a change of heart.

I put on the longest hair I had in my closet; at the time I was rocking a cute short bob like Cynda Williams in *Mo' Better Blues*. I slipped into a cute little green swing dress with a pair of multi-colored mules and a Chanel clutch.

Just because I was feeling crappy emotionally did not mean I needed to look like I felt that way. So, I made sure everyone knew that I was looking Hollywood and I made sure that every inch of that hair was swinging and bouncing when I moved. There was no denying that I had it going on that evening, at least on the outside.

I didn't recognize anyone there and decided that it was best to take a seat at the bar and enjoy the music.

At first glance you might have thought I was on a bender. Four empty shot glasses and some beer nuts sat strewn before me at the bar. Two of them were mine, but for some reason everyone's empty glass made its way in front of me, and the bartender was too busy to keep the area in front of me tidy.

It was not long before guys began their attempts to gain my interest. Maybe it was all those shot glasses sitting in front of me. Some sent over drinks, others came right over and introduced themselves, but I wasn't interested even in them or the drinks. Everything was perfect for a woman to meet someone that evening, but one by one, I turned them down. Normally, when I am with either of my girls, it never happens like this, but the one time I'm alone and engaged, God was sending them all my way. I guess it's like spotting a lone doe. The wolves were on the prowl.

Amidst all the attention, I noticed Greyson standing across the room. Without hesitation, I rushed over to him and threw my arms around him, squeezing him tightly. I was just glad to have someone there that I knew, a guy I could hang with to keep the others away. He returned the hug.

"How are you doing? And why so affectionate?"

"I'm doing wonderful now," punching his shoulder like a young schoolgirl.

"Really! Who are you here with?"

"I'm here by myself. Look at you! You look nice."

Greyson had his preppy look working, and for the first time I could see why he and Deco were best friends; he was just as handsome as Deco with his own unique twist on a look. Who knew? Greyson also had a brilliantly charismatic personality that left most people intrigued. He had hidden this part of himself at lunch. As I learned later, this bit of mystery was part of his charm, but it was not contrived in any way. It was just who he was—is.

"Let me introduce you. This is Omar. Omar, this is Kennedy."

"Hi Omar, it's a pleasure to meet you."

"You seem to be really excited to see Greyson."

"You have no idea!"

"Greyson, is this the same Kennedy you were telling me about?"

"Yes, it is!"

"This is the otherness? This is Naomi Campbell, Greyson?"

"I do not look like Naomi Campbell and what's the otherness?"

"Never mind that! Like hell you do not, you're a little lighter, but look at those legs!"

Some guy standing next to us overheard the conversation and shouted, "Man, I been watching Naomi all night. I hope she doesn't have her attitude though!"

"I assure you I don't!"

We all began to laugh, and the conversation flowed easily from there. It wasn't long before we had taken it into the hotel lobby. Omar must have realized right about then that the evening hanging with his boy should end. He made an excuse to leave.

"Greyson, I am about to leave. You two have fun."

"It was nice meeting you, Omar. But before you go, I have to know. What is this 'otherness' you were referring to?"

"I think I'll let Greyson explain it."

Greyson looked shocked; you could see he was carefully searching for the right words.

"You know how you have unicorns? Wait, a unicorn is something that doesn't exist, right?"

"Go on, I'm listening!"

"So, people are always searching for something that does not exist, i.e., the unicorn. Well, otherness is kind of like that, but it does exist. It can be a place, a thing or, in this case, you. It's something that's pleasantly different from anything one can imagine."

It was fun seeing Greyson squirm his way through the answer. I smiled at the response. Suddenly my night had taken a turn for the better.

In a matter of moments, Greyson and I were ditching the lounge and making our way downtown to dance. We went to a club that played electronic dance music. Little did he know that was one of my favorite types of music. Murphy and I used to dance all night to this music. Once I got on the dance floor, I let loose, I gave him my full Beyoncé. I twirled and swung my hair as I danced around him. Nothing too erotic or seductive, but I wanted him to notice me. At one point, as we danced, he was looking away, so I placed my hands on each side of his face and turned it toward me.

"I need you to look at me,' I said.

I don't know what came over me or why he appeased me; it had not been two weeks since I rejected Greyson's interest, yet none of that seemed to matter to him. It was just Greyson and me dancing, holding hands and exploring each other's thoughts for the rest of the evening.

The champagne flowed freely the remainder of the night and my mundane week had suddenly become perfect. The evening ended with plans for the next day. And the next day turned out to be every day.

Our friendship grew rapidly. We never went a day without seeing each other. The time I was spending with Greyson was so exciting I had completely forgotten about contacting Chase to give him an update on the house.

It had been three weeks since my last conversation with him and both of our life's was abruptly changing. But he hadn't contacted me either, which made me comfortable in the way I was feeling. I did not feel like we were drifting apart exactly, but it sure didn't feel like we were coming closer together.

Greyson and I were able to let our friendship flourish once Chase and I realized that the engagement was not going to work. It was a difficult decision because I'd sort of made a commitment to Chase and our future. But Chase had received a career opportunity with the mayor in Arkansas. It was the kind of opportunity that he could not pass up, not for the career uncertainty that awaited him in Florida, and there was no way I was moving back to Arkansas.

So that made a difficult decision easier. It was a no brainer, and the timing could not have been more perfect.

Sitting at the kitchen table, I thought about the conversation we'd had. Chase called forty minutes past the time we'd set for the call.

"Hey, Babe."

"Hey."

A long silence followed. I sat there wondering who was going to speak first.

"Chase, you were supposed to call forty minutes ago."

"I'm sorry. I got busy and lost track of time."

"What was so important that you couldn't call at the agreed time to talk about this wedding?"

"Before we start with the wedding, Kennedy, I'm seriously thinking of taking the position with the Mayor. I want to know how you feel about that."

"To be honest, I think that's great. I'm really happy for you."

"You're happy for me? Don't you mean you're happy for us?"

"I am happy for us, but I have my concerns."

"Everything is going to be fine; so, we need to discuss when you're returning to Little Rock."

I took a big swallow from the glass of wine that sat on the counter and thought about how I should formulate my response. Now was not the time to be analytical with my thoughts; honesty was the only card to be played.

"I don't think I can return to Arkansas."

We negotiated several half-hearted solutions, but neither one of us wanted to budge. It was never spoken, but we both knew we did not want to be married to each other. A part of me hurt after making the decision but looking back I knew when he proposed that we would never make it to the altar. Maybe I only said yes because my mother had met Chase and she thought fondly of him.

Once I hung up the phone I sat there pondering over my life. Without thinking I began to write down my thoughts about what had just taken place. At first, I was angry with Chase, but then I began to reflect on the places I had lived and experiences I had.

But why was I feeling angry? It was what I really felt was the right thing, wasn't it? And if Chase felt it too it must be the right thing. Maybe I was just feeling rejected; he didn't really want this either and I knew it, but I wanted it to be one-sided. I wanted to be the only one to do the rejecting. It was part of my self-entitled nature, I guess, the one I was raised with.

I thought of every blessing I had received, all of the angels that watched over me. Sure, some people would not understand my actions, and some would say I was careless and self-absorbed. But I know that was not the case. I am nothing like Phillip nor am I like my biological mother, Kim. I am the blessing to Mary and Earl, a couple who waited their entire marriage for a child. The couple who raised me to live every day as if I had already received the blessing and who taught me how to not live in fear or with boundaries.

And I had Greyson…at least for now.

It was okay to not want to live in the small town, and if someone felt I looked down on them because I did not want to be there then that was on them.

In that moment it all became clear to me. I had made a big difference to at least some people's lives. Most people were happy that I had entered their life, even if they were helping me and I was on the receiving end.

After reading what I had written, my thoughts inspired me. I knew what I needed to do; I knew what I wanted to do. I was going to help those in need. I'd verbalized this sentiment before, but now I was truly convinced that this should be my ultimate goal, my path in life. I'd been blessed many times over, and I wanted to be more of a blessing to more people.

Any attempt to keep my new purpose to myself quickly went away once I saw Greyson. I told him I knew what my purpose was but did not know how to position myself to succeed at helping others. That is when he suggested I become a Big Sister and see where it led.

It turned out that Greyson was the man of my dreams. He was understanding and patient with me even during the times I did not deserve his patience. He encouraged me to be there for Chase if the breakup became too difficult for him. He was unlike any man I had dated. He constantly thought of others before himself.

Greyson showed me the city, and it seemed like he knew everyone. It did not matter where we were or what we were doing. Someone he knew would invariably show up. I was finally starting to like the city of Orlando.

Even though we did not call it a date, he cooked dinner for me once. It was an utterly amazing seafood dish worthy of any 4-star restaurant. Afterward, I understood why he laughed the first time we met at Deco's 'outstanding' lunch.

Greyson's hands were gifted beyond belief; there seemed to be nothing he could not do with them. But what was more impressive was his relationship with his mother. He was very well mannered, and he treated his mother with the utmost respect.

He once told me how his father adored his mother, so he figured it was simply the way to treat a woman. When I met her, I found her to be very funny; she reminded me of my own mother. Greyson's family were close. They were middle-class, not uppity or snooty. Class and status did not seem to matter one bit to them. They were comfortable and confident in their own skin and didn't feel the need to put on airs or pretense.

Most importantly, to me at least, Greyson was caring and romantic. He constantly surprised me with beautiful gifts. He was everything I had dreamed of in a husband as a young woman. But I made sure not to allow myself to get carried away with that fantasy too soon.

I had seen it too many times before; a woman would meet a guy, go on a date and return home to start planning a wedding in their head. I always thought it was foolish of them, they knew good and well that they had chosen the wrong guy, yet there they were talking about a husband with their girlfriends. Maybe it was insecurity or a need to be with someone. Maybe it was peer pressure or the thought of being alone. I don't know. But even when she knew how that story would end, which was usually her crying uncontrollably from a pain that no one's religion could make go away, she did it anyway.

Greyson was different. He told me I was the first thing he thought of each morning. He wanted to make each of my days better than the one before, and he was making sure I knew it. To this day I still receive a just-because gift once a month from him. It could be something as simple as flowers or something extravagant like expensive jewelry or my favorite - a romantic dinner prepared by him.

Dating Greyson was like a dream come true to me; he was unlike any guy I had dated before--so much so that after the first time we made love, all I could say to him was, "Thank you, thank you, Greyson." His love was as wide as the ocean; it was like that place where it kisses the sky. It was like pure water falling over rocks in a mountain stream; it was fresh and fragrant and alive, and it was a fountain of life to me. I could feel every molecule of me being rearranged. My resistance to his love was nonexistent. All my fears of being loved and letting someone close had vanished. Greyson had captured my heart and kept it, and all my love was infected with him.

We would spend hours talking. We talked about everything. Even our moments of silence did not seem silent. The more we talked and spent time together, the more I began to realize just how smart he was and just how much I could trust him with my secrets. Most of our evenings were spent walking the beach. It was the one place we could completely relax and be ourselves without distractions or interruptions.

The rumble of the waves rushing ashore seemed to serenade us. We walked along the beach, feeling the warmth of the sand between our toes. Each beach house we passed seemed larger than the last; you could see the occupants of the homes in their kitchens or watching TV. Occasionally someone would be on their pool deck and they would wave and watch us pass.

Our favorite home was the modern home with a side garage that could be seen from the beach. Parked just outside the garage sat a white Porsche Carrera 911 convertible. Greyson stopped in his tracks. It was his dream car. He knelt, gathered a hand full of sand and slowly let it sift through his fingers, never losing sight of the vehicle and home.

"You know, one day I'm going to have a life like this! Let me correct that; we're going to have a life like this."

"Mmm hmmm."

I could see his demeanor had changed. He was focused and firm as he spoke. "Kennedy, I have dedicated my life to this vision, nothing will get in my way. I refuse to be one of those people who are constantly talking about what they are going to do only to go home and watch TV. Not me. Not me." Greyson stood to his feet and brushed the remaining sand from his fingers.

"I have a plan, and it doesn't include the firm. I am grateful for all they have given me; they have shown me that people live ways I had no idea existed. But I have a plan, a plan that will get us there. When we get married, I mean if you were to marry me, I would wake up with the purpose of making you happy. I would never be afraid to give all of myself to you. I'd fight Jesus Christ himself for you! Ok, now I'm talking crap, but we'd definitely have a strong relationship." He laughed in a way that made me believe that this was indeed possible. He spoke as though it were already true, and I remembered Mary's similar words.

"Thank you, Greyson, but right now you're in your feelings. Let me hear this plan."

I was not surprised that he actually had a plan, but I was surprised at the length of time it would take to execute—how real and solid it was.

Later that evening, I lay across my bed thinking about Greyson's plan. It was very detailed, every step well thought out. And I had no doubts about his ability to execute it.

I sprang to my feet once I remembered he'd given me his card. Retrieving the card from the stack of others I'd been given over the years; I noticed his card was different. The card was not a reproduction like all the others. The paper was of better quality, the logo was handmade, and all the calligraphy was handwritten and perfectly placed. It was the best handmade business card I had ever seen. It was the *only* handmade card I have ever seen.

Three days later, I met Greyson for a day of fun as usual. It was a day just like all the other days we had spent together, which meant everything centered on me.

"Before we start, I have great news Greyson. I met my first little sister and I also have something for you." Then I gave Greyson a check. He just stared at me as I placed it in his hands.

"What is this, Kennedy?"

"That is for you; it is for you to go to school and get your contractor's license."

"Kennedy, I can't take this from you."

"Why not?"

"Because that's your money and I'm not with you for your money. I will continue to save until I have it."

"Look, Greyson, I have noticed you take care of your parents. I have watched how you take care of me. You put everyone above yourself, you deserve this."

"Kennedy, I can't take this money; we haven't even known each other that long."

"Greyson, people have taken care of me all my life. People have blessed me even when I did not deserve it. I was not kidding the other day when I said I was going to dedicate myself to helping others, and no one is more deserving than you. You need money for school, and I just so happen to have money. It's just a tool--to be used, not hoarded. I believe in you, Greyson; and do not think I am giving you this money contingent upon us continuing to date. I am giving you this money so that you can achieve your dream and become the man I know that you are.

"Now, this is what you are going to do," I continued. "You are going to take this check, and you are going to enroll in the next class and not say another word about it. Then, you are going to take me to dinner because I am hungry. By the way, when did you make your business card?"

"It was a while ago. I made fifty of those cards, all identical, precise and perfect, to give to fifty people that I thought would somehow get me recognition or an opportunity for me to reach my dream." He took my hands in his. "Kennedy, you weren't supposed to get one of those cards, they were for business owners. I simply wanted you to have my number with the hopes of you calling. I never thought in a million years this would be happening. You're truly my beautiful otherness, Kennedy."

It was the best money I had ever parted with. That was the best seed I have ever sown. God has blessed me in so many ways from that seed. From that seed, my business has grown to something I could never have imagined.

"Obviously, your father and I married and had you, Kylie, our beautiful daughter. That same four thousand dollars allowed him to get his license, start a business, and grow it into the largest minority-owned custom builder in the southeast. It was the seed to my future; it was the seed to happiness. It was that happiness that gave me the strength to fund scholarships for twenty wonderful deserving kids, become a board member for the American Cancer Society and raise $3 million for heart disease and the homeless. That same seed of happiness also gave me the courage to do something I needed to do for many years."

THE THIN OLD MAN

I ASKED KYLIE TO GO to her room to finish getting ready. I did not want to share the last parts of my story with her because they involved Phillip.

"Kylie, it's time we finished getting dressed. The car service will be here any minute, and I don't want us to be late."

"Mom, it sounds like you are getting to the end and what might be one of the juiciest parts of your story. Can you save it for the car?" Kylie's interest was piqued.

I simply was not ready to share any parts of Phillip with her. "Maybe one day we will get to finish. But, for now, I need for all of us to get dressed and be ready to go get this award." I smiled from ear to ear. She obeyed and headed to her room.

Even though Greyson had been right by my side during this last painful part of my story, I still needed to get it out. Holding on to pain is the worst thing you can do to yourself and your family. It can cause you to do some crazy things, as I learned in my childhood and all throughout college. I was so grateful for Greyson coming into my life because he gave me the courage to do what I thought would be impossible. We were going to the prison to see Phillip.

Something in me did not feel right. I had been trying to prepare myself for this day for several weeks. But a sudden nauseating feeling appeared during the drive.

I sat in the car trying to calm myself while ignoring the nausea that was rising in my stomach. The grey building stood a hundred yards before us. Greyson held my hand, reassuring me that he was there for me during the process.

The phone rang just as we were about to exit the car. It was Deb, our office manager. Her call came at the perfect time. It was a much-needed distraction; any other time I would have surely let the call go to voicemail. Greyson could tell I was stalling. After a few moments of being patient, he gave me a look that let me know it was time to end the call and get on with it.

A green sign with white letters that read *Florida Department of Correctional Institution* was to the right of the walkway. The pebbles that filled the walkway crunched under my heels as we approached the building. My heart pounded.

The clock read eight fifteen when we were told we could enter. A loud startling buzzer sounded once we passed through the large metal doors. In an adjoining room, a guard sat watching monitors next to the waiting room in which Greyson and I were placed. All our personal belongings had been taken prior to us entering this room. We took a seat and I wondered if what was left of our dignity would be taken as well.

"Are you nervous?"

"A little bit," I answered and grinned.

"Just try and remain calm; you're tough, you can handle this."

"This is crazy, Greyson! I have not seen or spoken to this man since I was about six years old. If you were to have asked me then, I swear my answer would have been I'm never seeing him again, yet here I am."

"Well, you just say the word and this all ends. Do we need a code word? Washington DC, New York, IPO; I got it, Captain Crunch."

We both laughed.

"You're stupid! How am I supposed to work Captain Crunch into the conversation? But I appreciate you trying to cheer me up. I love you."

"I love you, too."

"I think I'm going to need a drink after this!"

All our laughter ended when Phillip walked into the room. My heart pounded. I did not know if I should hug him, punch him, or shake his hand. What if he tried to kiss me? Should I stay seated or should I stand? It's amazing how much can go through your mind in a matter of seconds, especially when you are nervous.

I am not certain what I imagined he would look like. In fact, I do not think I ever gave it any thought. But before me was this thin old man wearing a neatly pressed blue prison shirt. His thin arms hung from the sleeves making it appear much too large for him, like when you wore your father's shirt when you were a kid. His pants were just as neat, and his work boots were military shined.

At first glance, I thought he had freckles, but after a closer look I saw that his cheeks had skin tags, and a pair of wire-framed glasses sat on what must have once been a well-formed nose. You could tell that he was once handsome, but prison had conquered his appearance.

Phillip smiled as he approached us; it was at that moment I noticed it. A gold tooth! A gold tooth! Phillip had a freaking gold tooth! Thank God it was not directly in the front. I do not have any idea why I chose to focus on it. Why should I care how he chose to decorate his mouth? But I could not shake it.

We had to wait almost an hour to be cleared to see him and another twenty minutes just to leave the building, and the time did not pass quickly. For two hours, Phillip answered questions I asked about his background, his family, and health. Some of his answers seemed genuine at times and with others I got the impression he was being reserved. But then, the real Phillip reared his ugly head, and I knew why I had stayed away from him all those years.

"I can't believe it's really you. It's been too many years since I've seen you," he tried to reach for my hand, but I quickly pulled it away.

"I can't believe I'm here either. I had to see you to find my way back to peace." I was shaking inside.

"Well, what kind of peace can I bring you, little lady. You want an apology or something like that? You want me to beg you to be a part of your life?" He leaned in closer. "I wrote those people plenty of letters letting them know I was coming for you, that you were my daughter and not theirs."

"Don't you call them 'those people.' They were my parents, and you caused my father to have a heart attack from your horrible letters. You're disgusting!"

"I guess he was just weak-hearted if a few letters killed him," he laughed and snorted.

It took everything in me not to jump across the table and rip his head off. Greyson held my hand underneath the table to keep me from losing control. I think Phillip would have liked that - to see me fly off the handle the way he does. It may have made him proud. Chip off the old block and all that.

"I'm not here to listen to a recount of your slimy antics. I am not here for an apology nor do I want you as a part of my life. I am here to let you know that what Mary and Earl, my parents, did for me was something you never did and could never do. You and Kim may have been the reason I exist, but Mary and Earl are the reason I am alive. They gave me love, hope, the ability to dream, and I had everything I wanted and needed growing up. You took my father's life with your words, but you didn't break the spirit he left in me." I leaned in this time.

"You are an evil son of a bitch who deserves to rot in this hell hole for the rest of your life. I know you will never admit to killing Kim and the slew of other women; I know you will never care about all of the families you have destroyed. But as God is my witness, you will burn in hell for the things you've done."

I pulled back my chair to stand. Greyson stood with me, and we backed away. As we turned to leave, I could hear Phillip say, "I've already been to hell, and I loved it, baby girl."

He never would say if he killed my biological mother or if he had anything to do with her death. A part of me was glad he did not confess. I do not know if I could have truly handled it, especially when I think about all the lives that were destroyed because of him.

Phillip was a killer for sure, and that would never change. We knew that he killed Sheila, he tried to kill his lover in Miami, and he was a suspect in Kim's unsolved murder. His threats were the cause of Papa Earl's fatal heart attack. Both times I'd ever met Phillip, I'd met him in prison. But I was sure of one thing. I would not be visiting him in prison again—or anywhere—ever again. Of that I was certain.

We collected all our belongings and exited the prison much quicker than we'd entered. I was ready to get as far away from there and from Phillip as possible. I was ready to erase every single memory of that visit and him. From that day forward I promised to never talk about him again, never think about him, and never worry whether he would get out. He would no longer have that hold over me because I was committed to breaking the chain of Phillip that had kept me bound from childhood. I made peace in my soul, and I was ready to close the Phillip chapter forever.

I was emotionally exhausted, and I knew that what I was feeling was transferred to Greyson. We slid into an empty booth at a restaurant a few miles down the road. It was rather a desolate place with a view of the parking lot and not much else. The restaurant was empty except for one old man who sat at the counter drinking coffee. Who knew a prison visit could be so exhausting. It was as if I had been a prisoner myself for three and a half hours.

"Are you ready for that drink?"

"Yes."

We laughed, hoping to release all the day's anxieties and stress with a bottle of wine.

"A gold tooth, Kennedy?" Greyson spoke with a smirk.

"I know. A gold freakin' tooth!"

SOMETIMES LIFE HAS OTHER IDEAS

My mother always told me, "Kennedy, don't give up. Kennedy don't quit. You must hang in there."

I used to find it funny because most of the time she would do for me the things I didn't want to do, or she would pay someone to do them for me. At the time, it felt like she was bothering me; other times it felt as if she did them to keep me out of her hair, but she never would let me quit even if it meant putting an alternative in place. It wasn't until I became an adult that I began to understand just what she meant.

"Even if you fail, Kennedy, stay in the saddle! Every success story has a few chapters of failure." I would be like, "What's a saddle, Mom? What are you talking about, we don't have a horse?" I would test her on almost everything, and, like most parents, she would usually be correct.

To this day, it amazes me how people handle pressure; it is astonishing what it does to them. Some people conquer it and excel, and for others, when it arrives, they fold and give in. Some people flee to avoid it altogether. Pressure is one of the best things that can happen to you. It's what makes diamonds from coal. It's the sign that you're on the right track. It may be a signal alerting you to the fact that you need to change something in your life. Regardless of how it arrives, if you are patient and just stay in the saddle, it's reward can be truly amazing.

It had turned into the perfect day just as I had hoped. From the time spent at the pool and me and Greyson in the shower on our veranda earlier, to the time spent with Kylie sharing so many of the memories from my life, everything had been perfect. This day could not get any better. Yet, it was about to as we entered the hotel.

A quartet played soft music in the lobby. The three of us made small talk with the other attendees waiting to enter the ballroom. An usher patiently waited for us while we had a drink from the bar. He politely escorted us to a table in the front of the room. Taking our place at the table, we continued to chatter about my crazy past, our present life, and our future with Kylie, occasionally smiling, waving, and kissing passing guests on the cheeks.

I thanked Greyson for being an amazing husband and father. I thanked him often because he always gave so much of himself for his family. I noticed how eighteen years later he still started every day with the intention of making me happy. Greyson had made my life so much easier. I was so much happier than I probably would have been if he'd never come into my life, and for that I always thanked God and Greyson.

"Greyson, I need to ask you something. I may have asked you this before but for the sake of me, I cannot remember at this moment. When did you know that you wanted to be the type of man that you are?" I wanted Kylie to hear this as well, so I pulled my seat back a bit so she could lean over to listen.

"Well, in high school I was not the hot guy in school, so asking girls for a date wasn't always easy for me. I used to hang with my boys; they were the guys the girls were falling for. They were popular, light skinned with good hair, so the girls looked at them first.

"I did not do things to draw attention, and I didn't go out of my way to make someone notice me. I was a little darker than those guys, and during that time girls were really into light skinned guys. So, I began to sit back and observe. I would see how they would meet girls and how they treated them, but I never had the heart to do the same with the girls I went out with.

"There was this girl that lived a few streets over from my house. Her name was Karen Sudi, and she and her family moved to the neighborhood when we were in middle school. Karen had an older sister named Weida. Now, Weida was drop-dead gorgeous. No one ever asked Karen and Weida where they were from. We all just assumed that they were part Middle Eastern or Spanish.

"Because Weida was so pretty, no one ever gave Karen much attention. Plus, Karen was a big girl. She was that big kid that the other kids did not want around. None of the kids wanted her to sit with them on the bus, and they would never invite her to their parties, but I was always polite to her. Besides, my mother would kill me if she found out I was mistreating a young lady. I did not want any part of my mom's anger. A few years passed, and Karen and I were going into the eleventh grade. However, no one had seen Karen for the whole summer. In fact, I do not think anyone even thought about Karen the whole summer.

"One morning we were waiting at the bus stop for school, we got on the bus and took our seat. From the bus, we could see this girl running toward the bus, and we were all thinking who the hell is this because this person is fine, and she was getting finer the closer she got to the bus. As she got close enough, she stopped running, and by then everyone on the bus was staring and whispering, but we still did not know who the mysterious figure was.

"This girl was filling out every inch of those Sasson jeans. She had a coke bottle figure that screamed 'look at me' and she was wearing red pumps with lipstick that matched her shoes. When this girl got on the bus, all the guys started moving things to make space for her." Greyson moved his hands around as if he were re-enacting what had happened.

"The guys who were sitting together quickly moved to empty seats hoping she would sit with them. She looked around the bus and made sure everyone got a good look at her, then she walked over to the seat next to me. I stared out the window pretending not to notice her.

'Move over Greyson. Do you mind if I sit with you?' she said.

"I looked up and realized it was Karen. Karen was fine. Karen was fine as hell. She was drop-dead gorgeous. For a week all you heard on campus was, 'Who was the fine new girl?' I would say, 'Man, that's Karen!'

"About a month passed and Karen became my girlfriend, and it was all because I had treated her the same as when she was bigger. All those popular guys were asking how it happened. Outwardly, I had cultivated my status as 'the guy'. I was one of them now, but inside I knew I did not want to be anything like them.

"Our relationship had given me unwanted validation from my male peers, but it also made girls take notice. My parents had bought a car for me, so we started riding to school together. One morning, we got to school and headed for the library just like every other morning. Once we got in the library, she hit me with it."

"Um Greyson, I think we need to take a break."

"Like a dumb ass, I said, 'A break from what?'"

"From seeing each other."

"She said it with such conviction that I had no time to process what was happening. This was my first real girlfriend, and it was ending, I could feel the tears filling in my eyes. The bell rang and she walked away.

"During our ride home at the end of school, she told me that her entire life she had been the big girl that no one noticed, and for the first time she was now the hot girl that everyone noticed, and she wanted to truly experience it.

"It made sense to me. As much as I did not like what she was saying, I understood. That was when I decided that every girlfriend from that point forward would receive the absolute best version of me."

Greyson's story touched me. I knew how he admired the way his parents loved each other and how his father thought his mother was the most beautiful woman ever. He had told me about the other women he'd dated, and I'd seen photos of the flight attendant, Mia, and Nicole from college, but I had never heard the story of Karen. I wanted to hear more but Kylie chimed in.

"Dad, that was really sweet."

Interrupting Kylie, Greyson turned his attention toward me. He told me he had a surprise for me. Slightly confused, but not shocked at his awaited confession, Greyson stood and asked me to do the same. Holding my hands, he spoke.

"There are two things I need you to do for me right know. One, is to show me that beautiful Mona Lisa smile."

I was already grinning from ear to ear.

"Two, I really need you to keep your composure for what's next."

Before I could comply, a greeter appeared from the corner entrance. From his shadow out stepped Murphy. All I could do was scream and try not to cry as she advanced toward me. Murphy and I hugged, kissed, and jumped up and down like little schoolgirls.

"Thank you, Baby!" I rushed over to Greyson giving him a kiss and that smile he loved.

Everything was perfect I had everyone I loved with me. We took our seats. I trembled with joy, Kylie to my left, Murphy to my right and Greyson in front of me at the table. I could barely hold in the tears. The evening was all so overwhelming that I never even noticed the empty seat at our table. Had I noticed, I surely would have asked why it was there and why it was vacant.

We three ladies made a last visit to the ladies' room before the awards were to be handed out and I touched up my lipstick.

"How do I look, sweetie?" I looked over at Kylie then at Murphy and smacked my lips together several times to set the lipstick just right, all the while fanning myself in an attempt to settle down.

"You look beautiful as always, Mom. I have never been prouder of you than I am at this moment." Kylie's eyes watered. "I'm grateful to have heard your stories today. They helped me understand the woman you are."

Once we were seated at the table again, Kylie touched my shoulder and whispered, "I'm honored to be here to see you get this award,

Mom. And, one day, I plan to be up there, too, getting my Woman of the Year Award. I want to be just like you."

I was overwhelmed with emotion. I quickly blotted the tears with Greyson's handkerchief.

"I'm so proud of you, honey. It is about time this city recognizes you for all the work you do."

"Thank you, Greyson." I leaned forward trying not to disrupt my evening dress and gave my husband a quick peck on the lips.

"Mom, please do not cry again when you are on stage. You just got yourself together, so keep it together, please." Kylie joked as she rubbed my arm.

"Well, so that you know, having you, your father and Murphy here with me means more than any award."

The ballroom was packed with three hundred elegantly dressed people. The gala was one of Central Florida's largest black-tie events. It was being hosted by a large law firm that started the event to help raise money for children with cancer. They had grown the event into this massive fundraiser that was getting national recognition for its efforts, and I had partnered with them. The girl from the small city, whose father was a murderer, was being honored.

The event was known for who was in attendance. There were always countless celebrities in the audience, so I was extremely nervous. CNN and Don Lemon were covering and taking part this year, which made the butterflies in my stomach highly active. Greyson continued keeping me calm throughout the evening. He could tell I was nervous, but he stood his ground when I wanted to have another drink.

"No, Kennedy, not until after you're done."

A woman had come by and tapped me on the shoulder signaling it was time for me to make my way backstage. The time had come for them to announce Central Florida's Person of the Year. I stood backstage as the Master of Ceremonies read all my accomplishments, the money I'd raised, and all the things I had done for the city.

"I want to thank you and introduce to you Mrs. Kennedy Davenport!"

The room exploded with applause.

"Thank you for this award," I began. "There's so much more I want to do."

I gave a brief history of my past and explained that it was because of my past that I partnered with the city and started a scholarship in my mother's honor.

"The Mary Whitmore Scholarship is a fifty-thousand-dollar scholarship that will serve as a bridge to a life of success for the adopted."

At the end of the stage, I could see Kylie, Greyson and Murphy waiting for me. Once I was done, I walked over to them and kissed them.

I don't regret anything I have ever done in life or any choice that I have made, but there are moments when I'm consumed with regret for the things I did not do and the choices I was too afraid to make. We spend most of our life being afraid, afraid of rejection and failure, afraid of all that life has to offer us, afraid of who we are, of being found out. Afraid of other people. Looking back at my life, my heart is torn over the places I did not visit, the things I didn't do, the people I did not love and the love I did not extend. I sometimes wonder what might have been.

But I have learned that failure and sacrifice have led the way to any success I have ever had. They have given me everything. It was Phillip's failure and my biological mother's sacrifice that gave me this amazing life along with Mary and Earl's love and sacrifice, and I am finally at peace with all of that.

Another party isn't going to make me prettier, younger or more relevant. It won't reconnect me with some lost crossroads in my life, and it surely won't fix the parts of me that are broken.

As someone great once said, "Another dent in this car ain't going to make a whole lot a difference." At best, it is a reminder that you're still alive and lucky as hell.

Life will not wait for you to make up your mind. Time waits for no one and your life will pass in the blink of an eye. Live it now, follow your passions, and wait only for those you love. All your failures are meant to direct you to your success. Your beautiful tomorrow will be made of all your todays, so begin to embrace all that you experience in the name of life and love. You cannot know your potential unless you walk through the doors that open for you. And do walk through them, for on the other side you may find a beautiful otherness.

CPSIA information can be obtained
at www.ICGtesting.com
Printed in the USA
LVHW041330150621
690265LV00005B/51